stories to read—to treasure

BRIGHT HORIZONS:
a collection

BOOK 2

CHARLOTTE S. HUCK
HELEN M. ROBINSON
A. STERL ARTLEY
WILLIAM A. JENKINS
IRA E. AARON

Design by Susan Keig

SCOTT, FORESMAN AND COMPANY

COPYRIGHT © 1969 BY SCOTT, FORESMAN AND COMPANY,
GLENVIEW, ILLINOIS 60025.
All Rights Reserved. Printed in the United States of America.
Regional offices of Scott, Foresman and Company are located in Atlanta, Dallas,
Glenview, Palo Alto, and Oakland, N.J.

ACKNOWLEDGMENTS

BOOKS

Michael the Upstairs Dog
   Reprinted from MICHAEL THE UPSTAIRS DOG by Edward Ormondroyd, illustrated by Cyndy Szekeres. Copyright © 1967 by Edward Ormondroyd and Cyndy Szekeres and used by permission of the publisher, The Dial Press, Inc.

The Forty-Ninth Magician
   Copyright © 1966 by Samuel F. Babbitt. Illustrations: Copyright © 1966 by Natalie M. Babbitt. Reprinted by permission of Random House, Inc. and Brockhampton Press Limited.

Obadiah the Bold
   From OBADIAH THE BOLD written and illustrated by Brinton Turkle. Copyright © 1965 by Brinton Turkle. All rights reserved. Reprinted by permission of The Viking Press, Inc.

A Weed is a Flower
   From the book A WEED IS A FLOWER by Aliki. © 1965 by Aliki Brandenberg. Published by Prentice-Hall, Inc., Englewood Cliffs, New Jersey.

The King Who Was Too Busy
   Reprinted with permission of Farrar, Straus & Giroux, Inc. and The World's Work Ltd., THE KING WHO WAS TOO BUSY by Eugene Fern. Copyright © 1966 by Eugene Fern.

Nine in a Line
   Reprinted from NINE IN A LINE, From an Old, Old Folktale. Written and Illustrated by Ann Kirn. Arabic by Leila Leonard. By permission of W. W. Norton & Company, Inc. Copyright © 1966 by Ann Kirn.

JACKET ILLUSTRATIONS IN "COLLECTORS' ITEMS" SECTIONS

Abingdon Press for: *Run Away Habeeb!* by Gladys Yessayan Cretan, illustrated by Robert L. Jefferson, copyright © 1968 by Abingdon Press.

Atheneum Publishers for: *Do Tigers Ever Bite Kings?* Text copyright ©1966 by Barbara Wersba. Illustrations copyright © 1966 by Mario Rivoli. All rights reserved.
   Illustrations copyright © 1967 by Gaynor Chapman. From THE FOOLING OF KING ALEXANDER by Mervyn Skipper. Used by permission of Atheneum Publishers.

Childrens Press, Inc., for: PIRATES & PRIVATEERS by Edith McCall, illustrated by Felix Palm, published by Childrens Press, Chicago.
   SIX FOOLISH FISHERMEN by Benjamin Elkin, illustrated by Katherine Evans, published by Childrens Press, Chicago.
   THE TRUE BOOK OF DOGS by Elsa Posell, illustrated by Betsy Warren, published by Childrens Press, Chicago.

Thomas Y. Crowell for: Jacket illustration by Ezra Jack Keats for *The Rice Bowl Pet,* by Patricia Miles Martin. Copyright © 1962 by Ezra Jack Keats. Reproduced by permission of the publishers, Thomas Y. Crowell Company, New York.

E. P. Dutton & Co., Inc., for: Jacket of THE HOLE IN THE TREE written and illustrated by Jean George. Copyright, ©, 1957 by E. P. Dutton & Co., Inc. Reproduced by permission of the publishers.

Garrard Publishing Company for: *Booker T. Washington: Leader of His People* by Lillie G. Patterson, illustrated by Anthony D'Adamo, copyright © 1962 by Garrard Publishing Company.
   George Washington Carver: Negro Scientist by Samuel and Beryl Epstein, illustrated by William Moyers, copyright © 1960 by Samuel and Beryl Epstein.

Harper & Row, Publishers Incorporated, for: Jacket illustration by Ezra Jack Keats for HOW TO BE A NATURE DETECTIVE by Millicent Selsam, Harper & Row, Publishers.

Houghton Mifflin Company for: *The Emperor's New Clothes* by Hans Christian Andersen, illustrated by Virginia Lee Burton, copyright 1949 by Virginia Lee Demetrios.

J. B. Lippincott Company for: The dustcover illustration for ONCE UPON A MOUNTAIN, written and illustrated by Don Bolognese. Copyright © 1967 by Donald Bolognese. Published by J. B. Lippincott Company and reprinted with permission.

Lothrop, Lee & Shepard Co., Inc., for: *Hear Ye of Boston* by Polly Curren, illustrated by Kurt Werth, copyright © 1964 by Lothrop, Lee & Shepard Co., Inc.

Hide and Seek Fog by Alvin Tresselt, illustrated by Roger Duvoisin, copyright © 1965 by Lothrop, Lee & Shepard Co., Inc.

Pick a Raincoat, Pick a Whistle by Lillian Bason, illustrated by Allan Eitzen, copyright © 1966 by Lillian Bason and Allan Eitzen.

McGraw-Hill Book Company for: *Adventure at Mont-Saint-Michel,* written and illustrated by Napoli, copyright © 1966 by McGraw-Hill Book Company.

The Happy Lion by Louise Fatio, illustrated by Roger Duvoisin, copyright 1954 by Louise Fatio Duvoisin and Roger Duvoisin.

The Golden Touch by Nathaniel Hawthorne, illustrated by Paul Galdone, copyright © 1959 by Paul Galdone.

William Morrow and Company, Inc., for: *Henry Huggins* by Beverly Cleary, illustrated by Louis Darling, copyright 1950 by William Morrow and Company, Inc.

Mr. Moonlight and Omar by James Holding, illustrated by Aliki, copyright © 1963 by James Holding.

Peter's Brownstone House by Hila Colman, illustrated by Leonard Weisgard, copyright © 1963 by Hila Colman.

Parents' Magazine Press for: *A Thousand Lights and Fireflies* by Alvin Tresselt, illustrated by John Moodie, copyright © 1965 by Alvin Tresselt.

Prentice-Hall, Inc., for: From the book, THE STORY OF JOHNNY APPLESEED by Aliki Brandenberg, © 1963 by Aliki Brandenberg. Published by Prentice-Hall, Inc., Englewood Cliffs, N.J.

From the book, THE STORY OF WILLIAM PENN by Aliki Brandenberg. © 1964 by Aliki Brandenberg. Published by Prentice-Hall, Inc., Englewood Cliffs, New Jersey.

Random House, Inc., for: *Look Out for Pirates!* by Iris Vinton, illustrated by H. B. Vestal, copyright © 1961.

William R. Scott, Inc., for: Title: BITS THAT GROW BIG. Author: Irma E. Webber. Artist: Irma E. Webber. Copyright Date: 1949. Copyright Owner: Irma E. Webber. Permission granted by: William R. Scott, Inc.

The Viking Press, Inc., for: From LION written and illustrated by William Pène du Bois. Copyright © 1956 by William Pène du Bois. Reproduced by permission of The Viking Press, Inc.

From SKI PUP by Don Freeman. Copyright © 1963 by Don Freeman. All rights reserved. Reprinted by permission of The Viking Press, Inc. From TWO HUNDRED RABBITS by Lonzo Anderson and Adrienne Adams. Copyright © 1968 by John Lonzo Anderson and Adrienne Adams Anderson. All rights reserved. Reprinted by permission of The Viking Press, Inc.

Frederick Warne & Co., Inc., for: "The Valiant Chattee-Maker." Copyright © Christine Price 1965. Published by Frederick Warne & Co., Inc.

The World Publishing Company for: *In a Garden,* written and illustrated by Ann Kirn, copyright © 1967 by Ann Kirn.

Lions in the Grass by Phyllis S. Busch, photographs by Arline Strong, text copyright © 1968 by Phyllis S. Busch, illustrations copyright © 1968 by Arline Strong.

COVER PHOTOGRAPHY by James Ballard. Concept of theme for cover by Raymond Barnhart.

3

CONTENTS

A COLLECTION 7
MICHAEL THE UPSTAIRS DOG
    by EDWARD ORMONDROYD
  About the Author............... 10
  About the Book................. 12
  Contents....................... 15
  Thinking It Over............... 59
  Talking It Over................ 60
  What Did the Author Mean?...... 61
  On Your Own.................... 62
  My Dog........................ 64
    by MARCHETTE CHUTE
  Tug of War.................... 65
    by KATHLEEN FRASER
  Collectors' Items.............. 66

THE FORTY-NINTH MAGICIAN
    by SAMUEL F. BABBITT
  About the Author............... 68
  About the Book................. 76
  Contents....................... 79
  Thinking It Over............... 117
  Talking It Over................ 118
  Taking a Look at Art........... 120
  Discovery..................... 122
    by HARRY BEHN
  Poem........................... 123
    by MICHAEL PATRICK
  Collectors' Items.............. 124

OBADIAH THE BOLD
    by BRINTON TURKLE
  About the Author............... 126
  About the Book................. 128

Contents 130
Thinking It Over 156
Talking It Over 157
A Long Ago Story 158
What's in a Name? 159
The Question 160
    by KARLA KUSKIN
Captain Jim 161
    by RACHEL FIELD
Until I Saw the Sea 162
    by LILIAN MOORE
All Aboard for Bombay 163
    by LEROY F. JACKSON
Collectors' Items 164

A WEED IS A FLOWER
    by ALIKI
About the Author 166
About the Book 168
Contents 173
Thinking It Over 201
Talking It Over 202
On Your Own 203
About the Pictures 205
Weeds 206
    by CHARLOTTE ZOLOTOW
The Seed 207
    by AILEEN FISHER
Three Poems 208
    by HARRY BEHN
    by RANSETSU
    by BUSON
Dandelion 209
    by HILDA CONKLING
Collectors' Items 210

THE KING WHO WAS TOO BUSY
    by EUGENE FERN
    About the Author................. 212
    About the Book................... 214
    Contents......................... 216
    Thinking It Over.................. 263
    Talking It Over................... 264
    Complete the Sentences............ 265
    Compare and Contrast.............. 267
    Looking at Pictures............... 268
    Real or Make-Believe?............. 269
    The King of Umpalazzo........... 270
        by MARY ANN HOBERMAN
    If I Were King................. 272
        by A. A. MILNE
    Collectors' Items................. 273

NINE IN A LINE
    by ANN KIRN
    About the Author................. 274
    About the Book................... 276
    Contents......................... 279
    Thinking It Over.................. 307
    Talking It Over................... 308
    What Makes a Folk Tale?........... 309
    People of the Desert.............. 311
    Let's Pretend..................... 312
    The Camel....................... 315
        by OGDEN NASH
    Arithmetic...................... 316
        by CARL SANDBURG
    Collectors' Items................. 318

SUMMER READING................... 320

A COLLECTION

What kind of stories do you like to read? Tales of magic? Funny tales? Stories about kings and princesses? People who lived long ago? Real people? Whichever stories you like most, you'll find them in this book. *Bright Horizons* is a collection of six books. Each of the books in the collection is one that you might find in a library or bookstore.

What kind of reader are you? Do you think you are a good one? A good reader doesn't just read lots and lots of books; he thinks about what he reads. Here are some questions a good reader asks himself:

    1. Why did the author write this book? Was it written for me to enjoy? Was it written for me to enjoy and learn something?

2. Is the author trying to give me something to think about?
3. Is this a true story, or did the author make it up?
4. How does the author tell his story?
5. Do the characters act like real people? Do they act like anyone I know?
6. What do the illustrations tell me?
7. Why did the author use certain words?

You can be a better reader when you finish *Bright Horizons*. This book will show you how by helping you think about the stories you have read.

Before each story there is an article about the author. Following this there is an introduction to the story. It will give you a hint about what you are going to read. Sometimes it will tell you what to look for in the story.

At the end of each selection there are

questions and suggestions to help you think carefully about what you have read. These questions are followed by some poetry for you to enjoy and a list of good books for you to read.

If you have a *Bright Horizons* notebook, you may put all your written work and drawings in that. If you do not, you should have a notebook of your own for just that purpose.

Begin reading now, and add to your collection of treasures—whatever they may be—shells, rocks, marbles, dolls. Maybe you will even want to start a different kind of collection—a collection of books. Books can be bright, shiny treasures—even on rainy days.

EDWARD ORMONDROYD was born in 1925 in Wilkinsburg, Pennsylvania.

He attended the University of California at Berkeley, California. He still lives in Berkeley with his wife and their three children, Evan, Kitt, and Beth.

Mr. Ormondroyd is especially interested in birds, poetry, and music. He says that he once saw a German shepherd and a specially built ladder in a backyard. Putting the two together and adding his own desire to live in the country, he wrote the story of Michael.

Michael the Upstairs Dog

by Edward Ormondroyd
Illustrated by Cyndy Szekeres

Do you have friends who are allowed to do things you aren't? If so, you have something in common with Michael. Michael is a German shepherd whose friends call him "the upstairs dog." Can you think of a reason why they might have given him this nickname?

The Dial Press, Inc.
New York

Michael
the Upstairs Dog

by Edward Ormondroyd

Illustrations by
Cyndy Szekeres

Reprinted from MICHAEL THE UPSTAIRS DOG
By Edward Ormondroyd, illustrated by Cyndy Szekeres
Copyright © 1967 by Edward Ormondroyd and Cyndy Szekeres
And used by permission of the publisher, The Dial Press, Inc.

Every morning before breakfast, Mrs. Wood took Michael the German shepherd for a walk around the block.

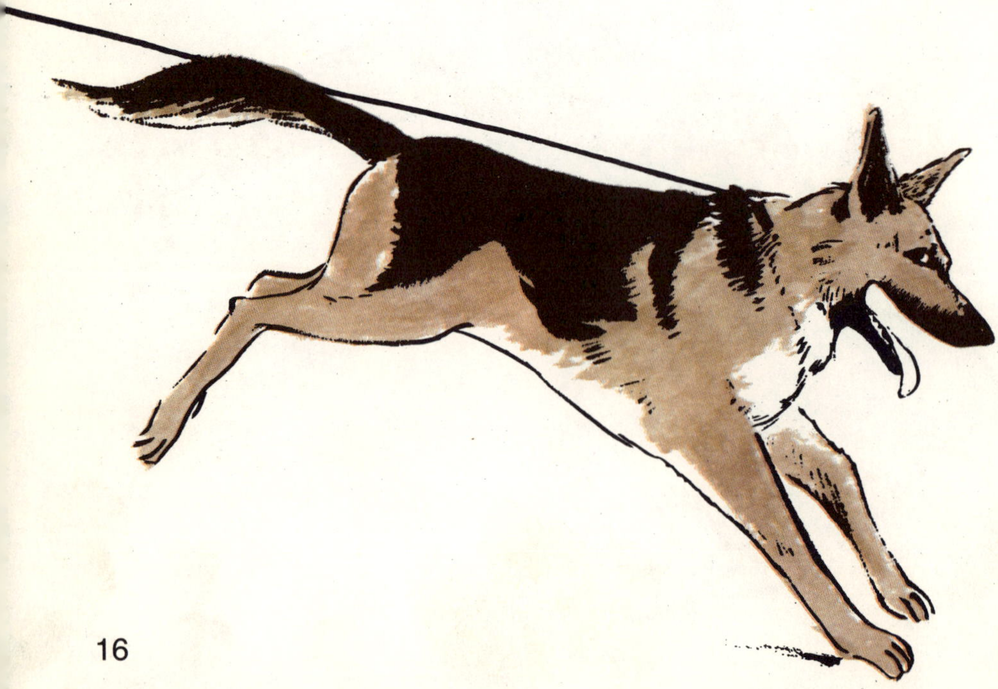

Every evening after dinner, Mr. Wood took him for another walk around the block.

But all day long, from breakfast time to dinner time, Michael had to stay indoors while the Woods went to work. They could not leave him in the backyard. There were no stairs from it to their second-floor apartment, and Mrs. Quist, who lived below, would be sure to complain if he were left there all day.

18

So Michael spent the day hanging out of a front window of the apartment, watching people and cars go by and waiting for the Woods to come home.

There were other dogs in the neighborhood who were allowed to run in the street. Michael talked to them when they went by. They called him Michael the upstairs dog.

One evening Mrs. Wood looked at Michael's sad brown eyes and said, "A dog like Michael ought to live in the country, where he could run around all day—don't you think?"

"Um," said Mr. Wood.

"I'd like to live in the country," Mrs. Wood said.

Mr. Wood hid behind his newspaper.

But after dinner, while he was taking Michael for his walk, Mr. Wood had an idea.

The following Saturday morning he was very busy with his saw and hammer and nails.

"All right, Michael," he said. "Now if you want to run around, you can climb down into the backyard."

Me climb *that?* Michael thought. Never!

Mrs. Wood stood at the upstairs window with a juicy bone. Mr. Wood boosted Michael up the bottom of the ladder.

"It's easy-pie," he said. "First one paw and then the other—just like walking up stairs."

Mr. and Mrs. Wood were so anxious for Michael to climb the ladder that he tried it just to please them. Once he had the knack of it, he felt proud of himself. There can't be many dogs with their own private ladders, he thought.

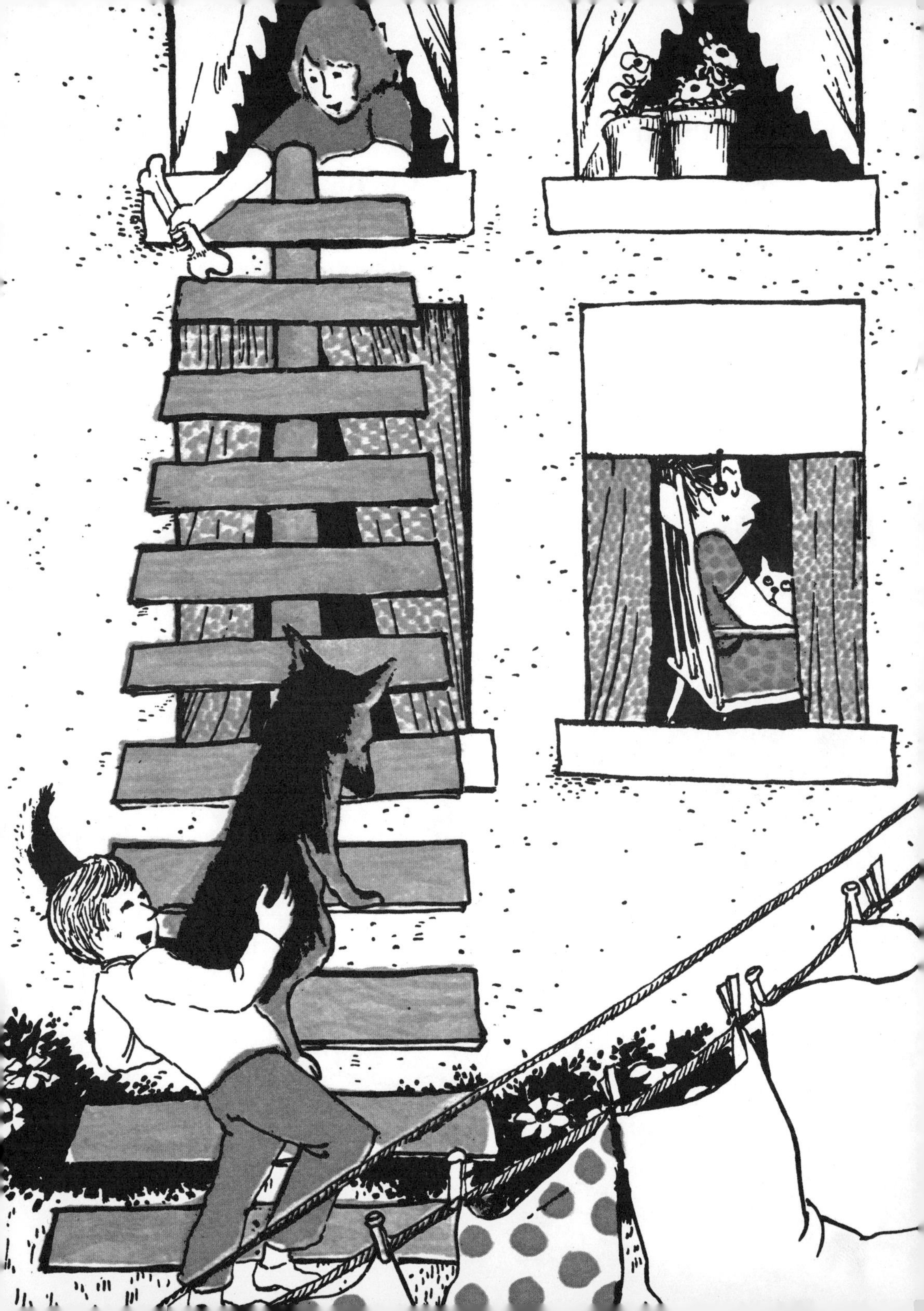

But the backyard was a dull place. Michael couldn't see over the high fence, and Mrs. Quist was always yelling at him from her kitchen window. "Don't run through my flower beds!

"Don't jump on my laundry!"

"Don't chase my birdies!"

So while Michael climbed down and up his ladder every day to keep in practice, he still preferred to hang out of the upstairs front window.

"Poor Michael!" Mrs. Wood said. "Look at those sad brown eyes! It just isn't like running around in the country, is it?"

"All German shepherds have sad eyes," Mr. Wood said. "It doesn't mean a thing."

"Well, I *still* think that if we lived in the country—"

"Um," said Mr. Wood, hiding behind his newspaper.

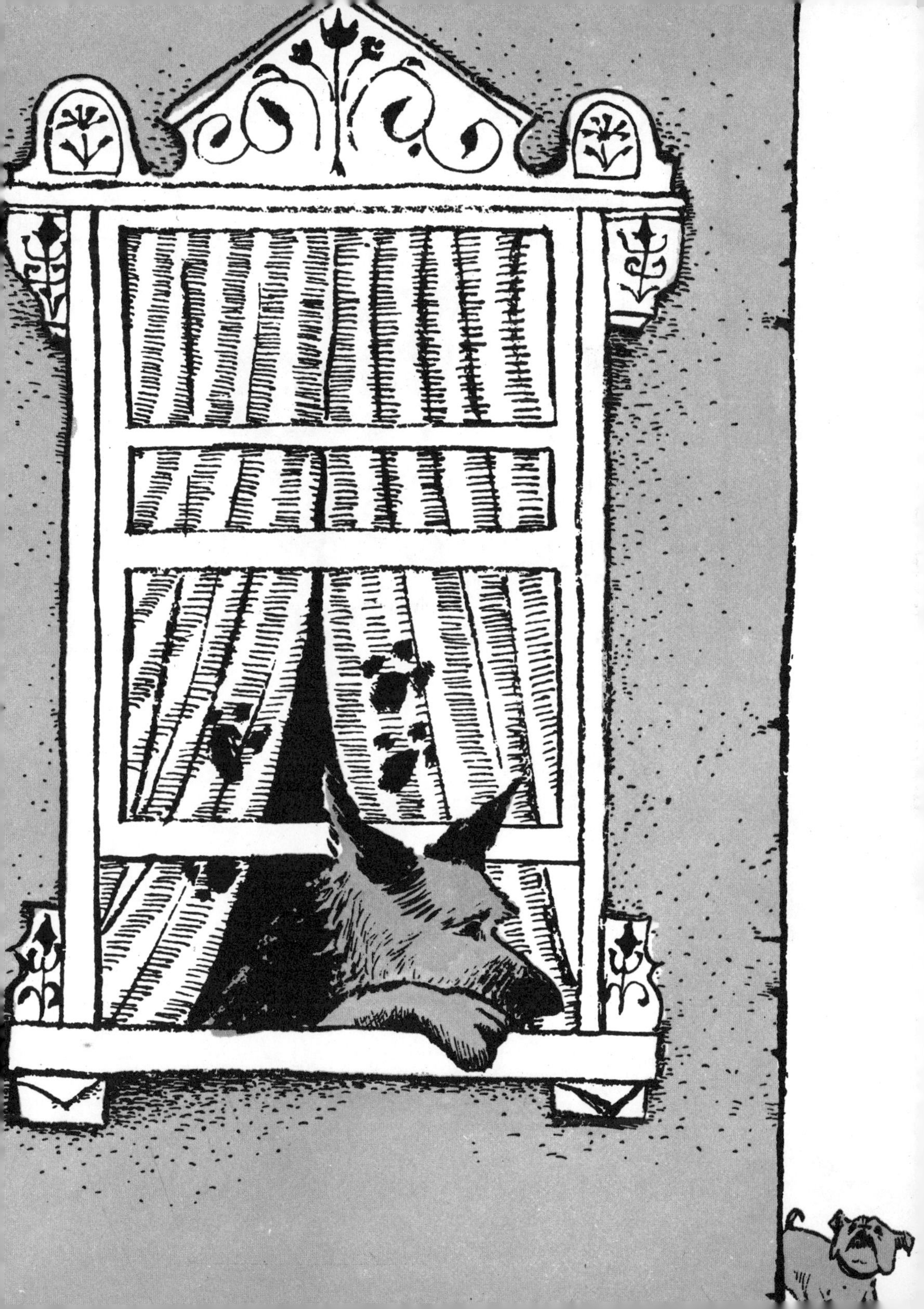

One day Mrs. Quist forgot to latch the gate to the backyard.

Feeling very excited at being on his own, Michael trotted out into the street.

In the next block he met his friends, Butcher the bulldog and Jacques the poodle.

"It's Michael the upstairs dog!" they shouted. "What are you doing out here by yourself, Michael?"

"I have my own private ladder now," Michael said.

"What's that?" they asked.

"It's a kind of—it goes up from the— you put your paws on the— Oh, come and see for yourselves," said Michael.

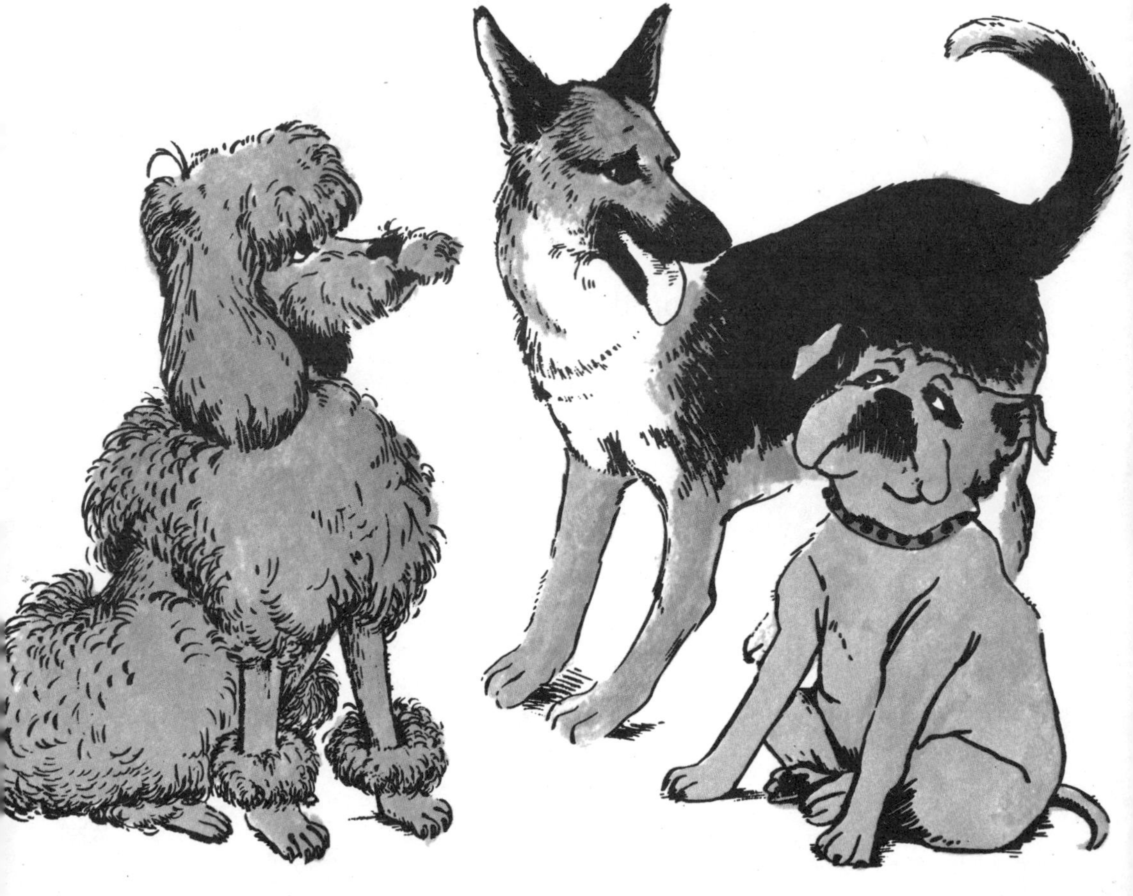

The news spread quickly that Michael the upstairs dog had something unusual in his backyard. A crowd of dogs began to collect behind him. By the time they got to Michael's house, there were so many dogs that they could hardly squeeze into the backyard.

33

"There it is," Michael said proudly. "Want to try it?"

"*Me* climb *that?*" Butcher said. "Never!"

"It's easy-pie," Michael said. "First one paw and then the other—just like walking up stairs. I'll show you."

And he did.

"I can do that," said Jacques. And up the ladder he went after Michael.

Seeing how easy it was, the other dogs began to climb the ladder, too. Even Butcher went up, keeping his eyes tightly closed so as not to get dizzy.

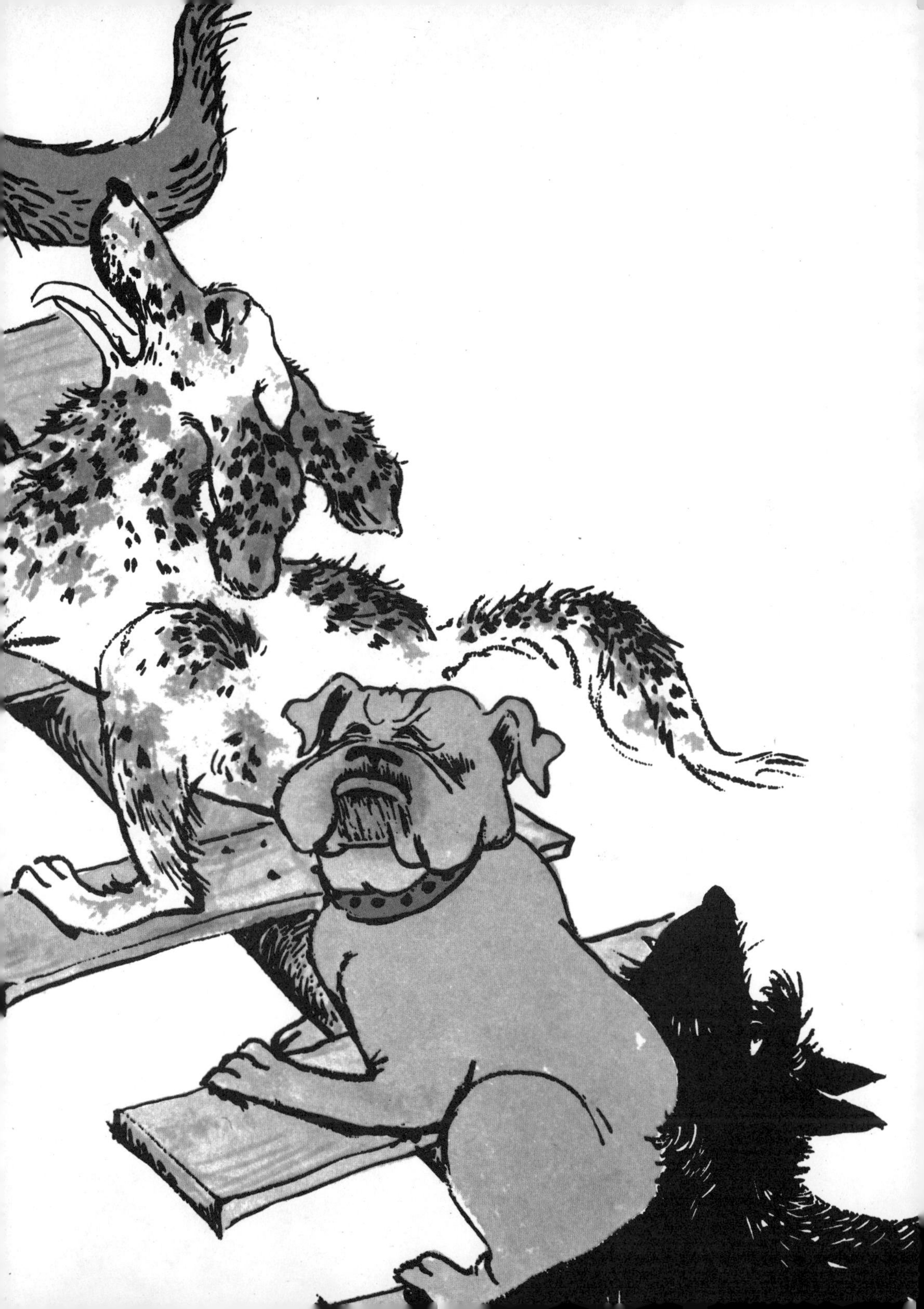

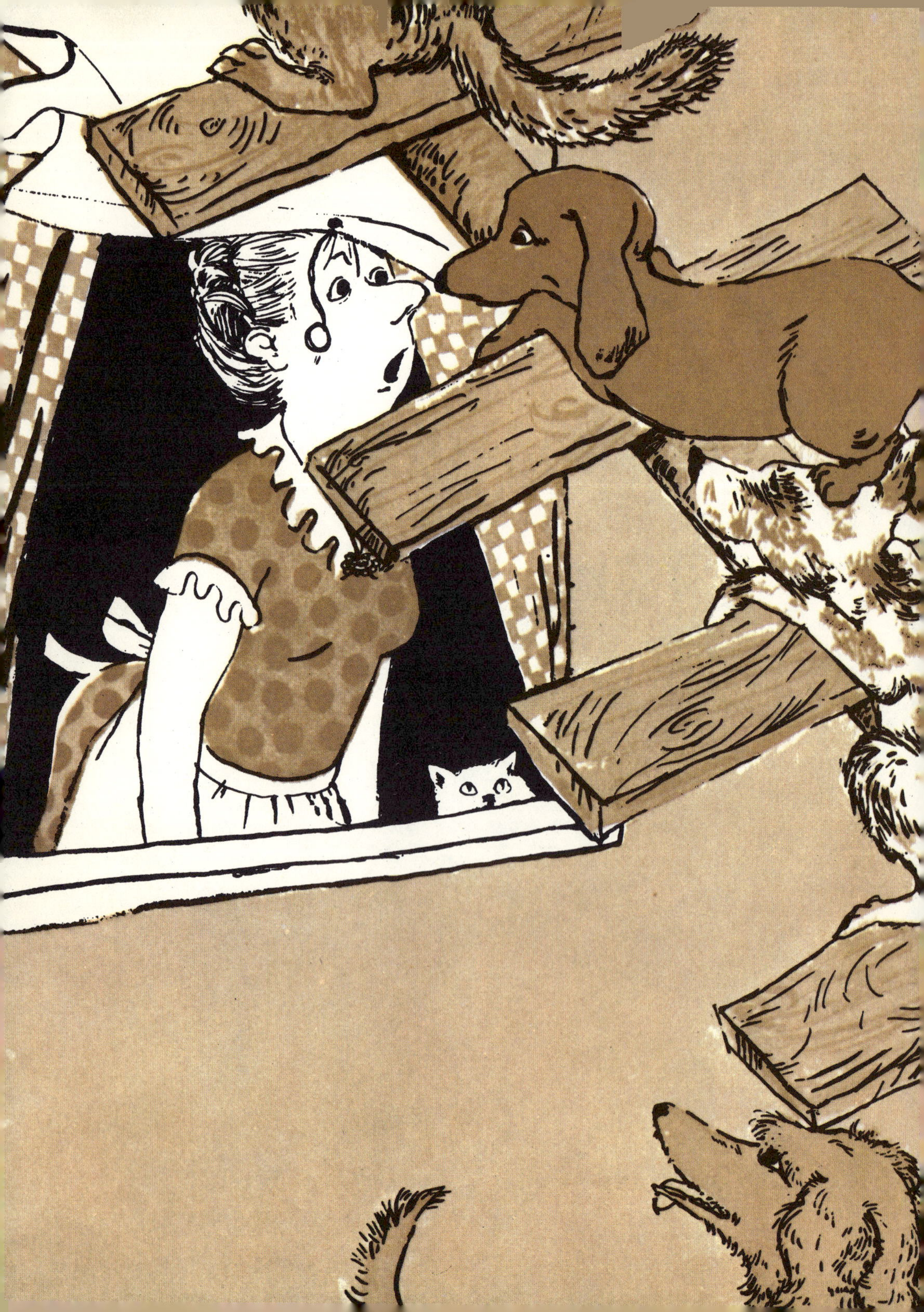

Just then Mrs. Quist glanced out of her kitchen window. "Oh, my goodness gracious sakes alive!" she gasped. "Something must be done!" She hurried to the telephone and called Mr. and Mrs. Wood. Then she called the landlord.

Michael thought something must be done, too. Things seemed to be getting out of hand. The dogs were beginning to explore the apartment, and they paid no attention to Michael when he begged them to go home.

37

"We used to have a refrigerator like this," Jacques said. "But after I learned how to open it, my master bought another kind. All you have to do is push this thing."

"Wow! Look at those pork chops!" said an Airedale.

"Look out!" Butcher growled. "I saw them first!"

Instantly a dozen dogs began to fight.

"Stop that! Get off my property!" Michael shouted. He seized a dachshund by the neck and tried to carry him to the ladder. But so many dogs were still scrambling through the window that he couldn't even get close.

Some other dogs had found the laundry basket and were beginning a tug of war with Mrs. Wood's bathrobe. Michael was knocked down in the struggle, and the dachshund wriggled free.

The fight around the refrigerator and the tug of war turned into a general free-for-all. The din was so terrific that Michael couldn't hear himself yelling for help.

"*Michael!*" Mrs. Wood shrieked, standing in the front door. "*What* is going on here?"

Mr. Wood charged into the apartment, beating right and left with a rolled-up newspaper. "Get out, get out!" he cried.

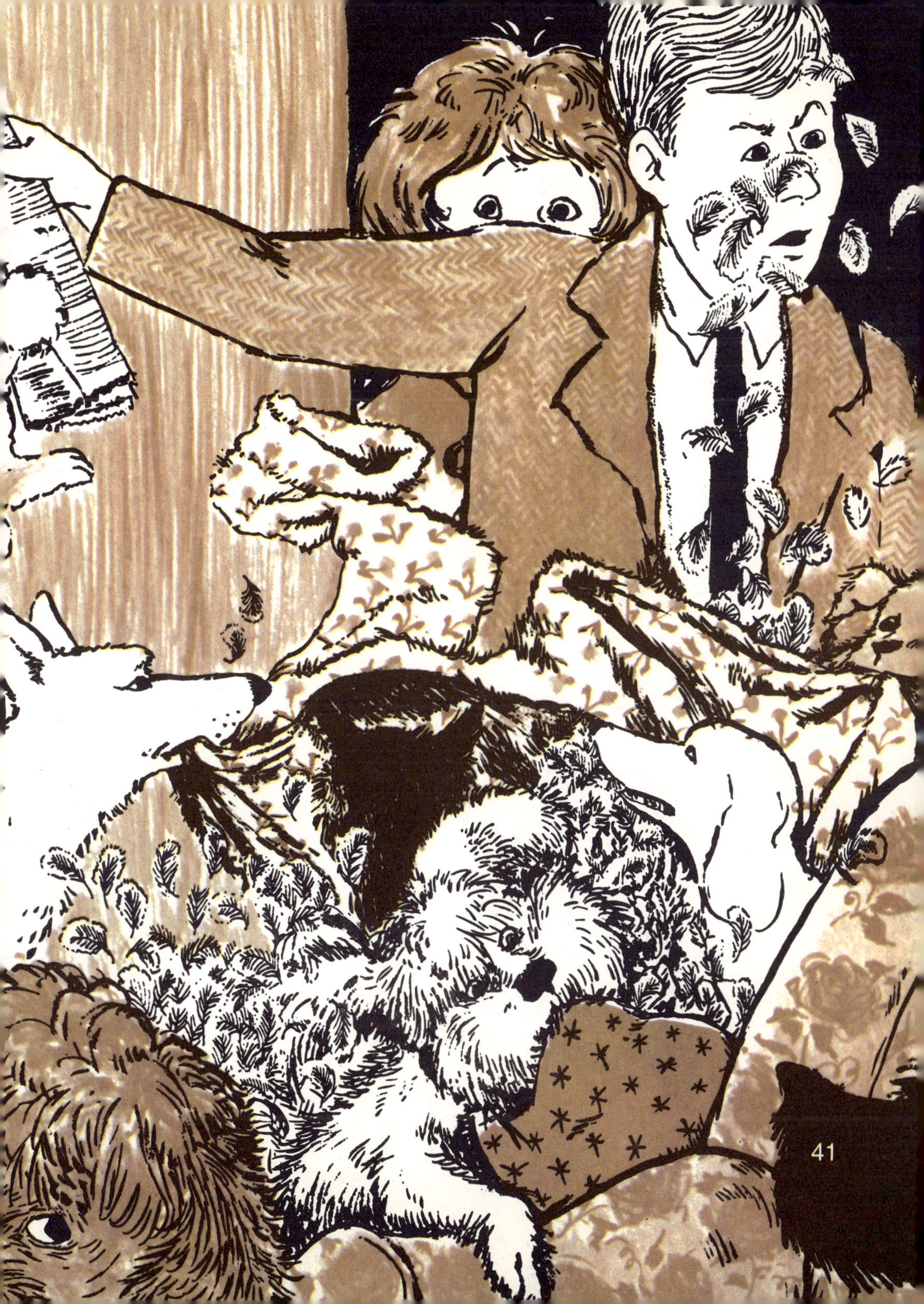

An avalanche of dogs poured down the stairs, right over Mrs. Quist and the landlord.

43

"What's the meaning of this?" the landlord shouted when he could stand again.

"Oh, dear!" Mrs. Wood said. "I don't know."

"It looked like every dog in town," said Mr. Wood, scratching his head. "But I don't know how they got in."

"*You* let them in!" Mrs. Quist cried. "They came up your ladder!"

"*Ladder?*" said the landlord. "What ladder?"

"Well," Mr. Wood said with a sigh, "I guess it's easier to show you than to explain."

Mr. Wood did not want the landlord or Mrs. Quist to see what a mess the dogs had made in the apartment. So he led them downstairs and around to the backyard to see the ladder.

Meanwhile Michael was feeling so upset that he crawled into his favorite thinking-place. There he found Jacques.

"I thought the pork chops would be out of danger here," Jacques explained with his mouth full.

"What am I going to do now?" Michael moaned.

"When *my* master is angry, I just disappear," Jacques said. "It's the best thing."

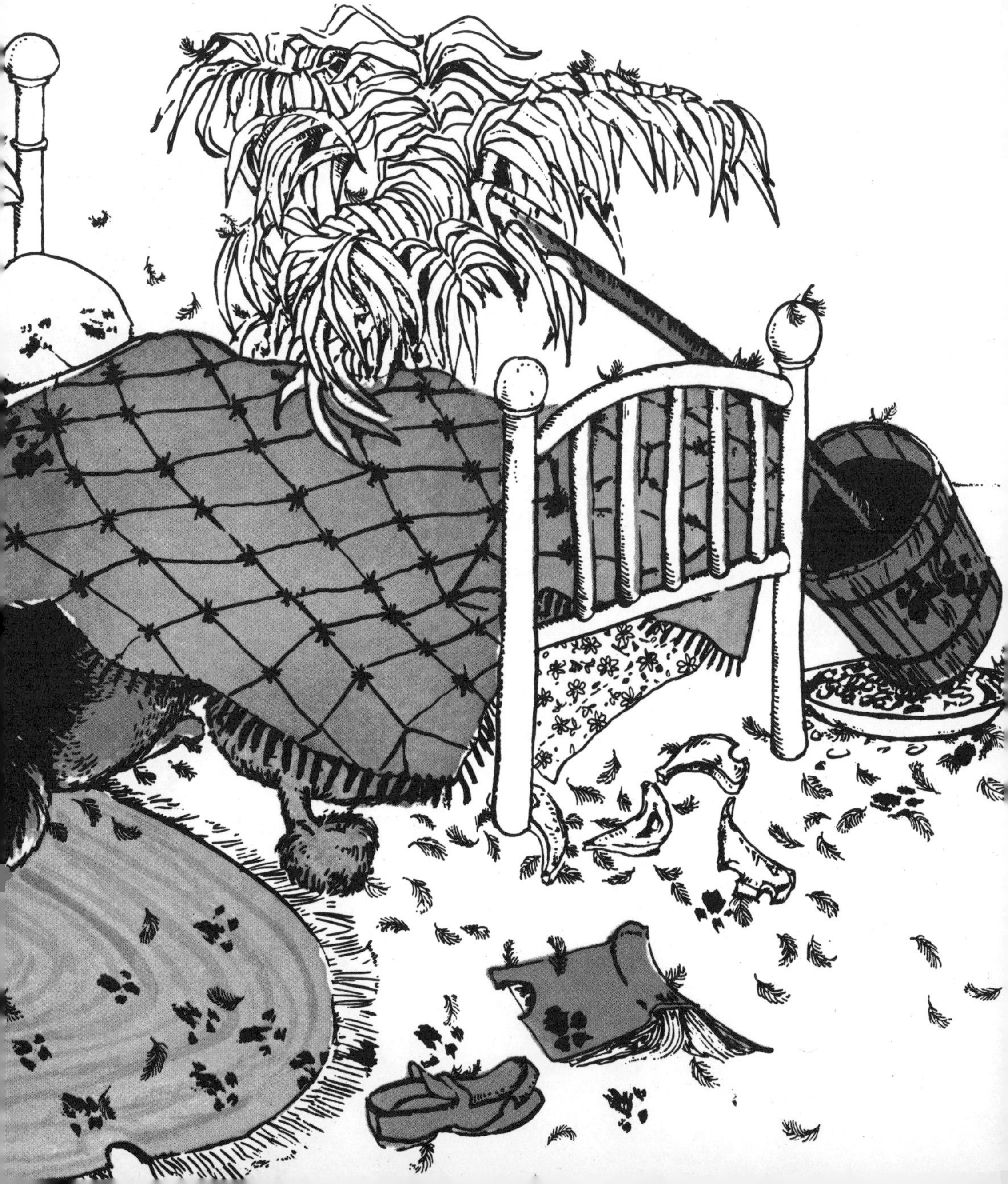

"But I've never run away before."

"You don't actually run away," Jacques explained. "It's only fair to give people a chance to calm down. They're always glad to see you when you get back. Come on, I know some good hiding places."

Jacques seized the rest of the pork chops, and they ran for the ladder. They didn't notice that the weight of all the dogs had loosened the nails and split the wood.

"Look out!" Jacques cried.

"Oh, no!" Michael yelped.

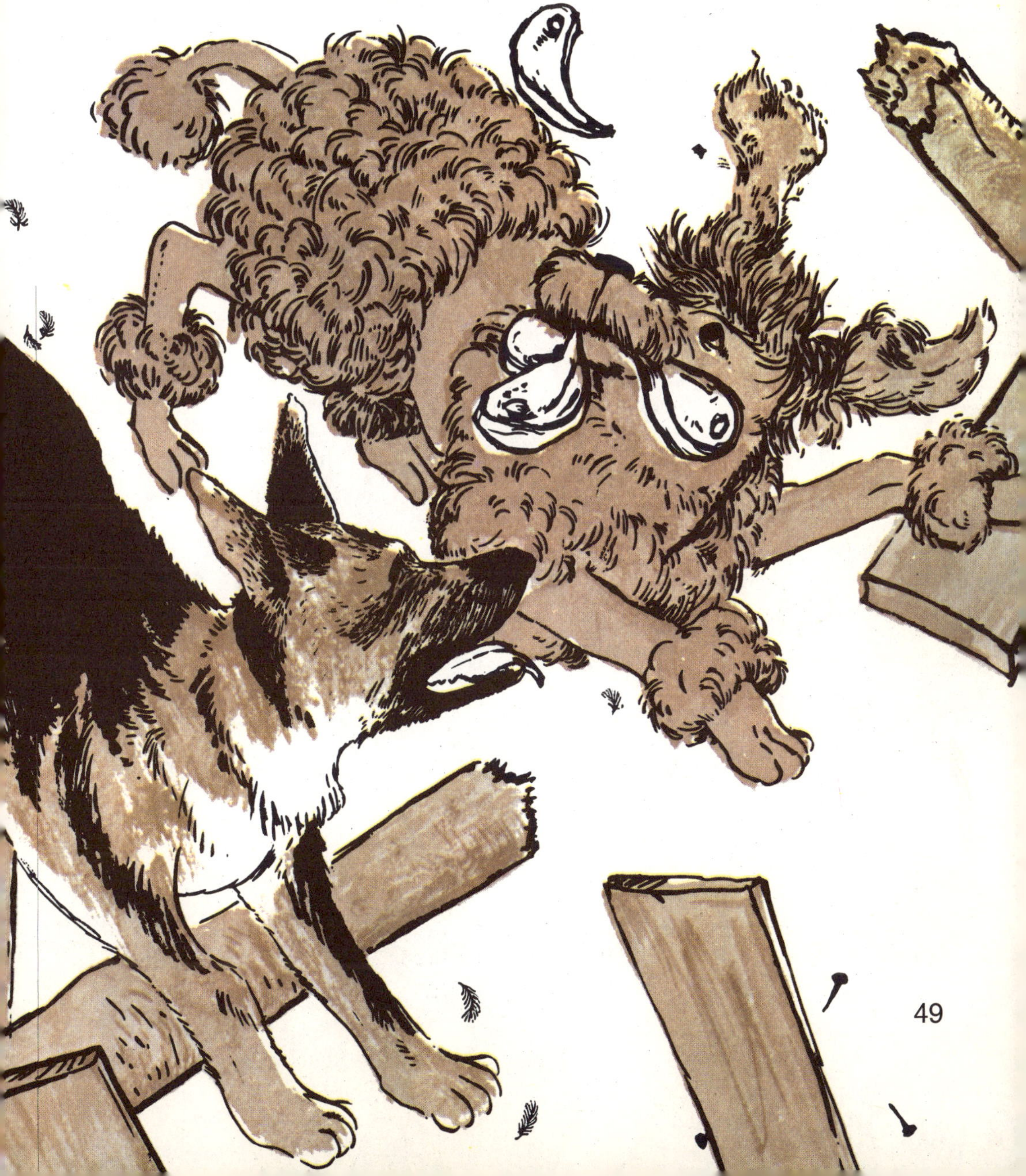

And just as Mr. and Mrs. Wood and
Mrs. Quist and the landlord came around
the corner of the house, down came Michael
and the ladder and Jacques and the pork

chops, right on top of them. The ladder also brought down the clothesline, which was full of Mrs. Quist's washing, and knocked over the garbage can.

"I do not rent my apartments to circuses!" the landlord shouted. "You have thirty days to move out of here!"

"But—" said Mr. Wood.

"But—" said Mrs. Wood.

"Thirty days!" the landlord repeated as he slammed his way out of the gate.

"Serves 'em right," Mrs. Quist muttered, going back to her kitchen.

Jacques scrambled over the fence and vanished.

Michael lay down in the wreckage and howled.

Mr. and Mrs. Wood had a long discussion while they picked up the washing and cleared away the pieces of ladder and put the garbage back into the can. Mr. Wood did not have his newspaper to hide behind, so Mrs. Wood had the last word.

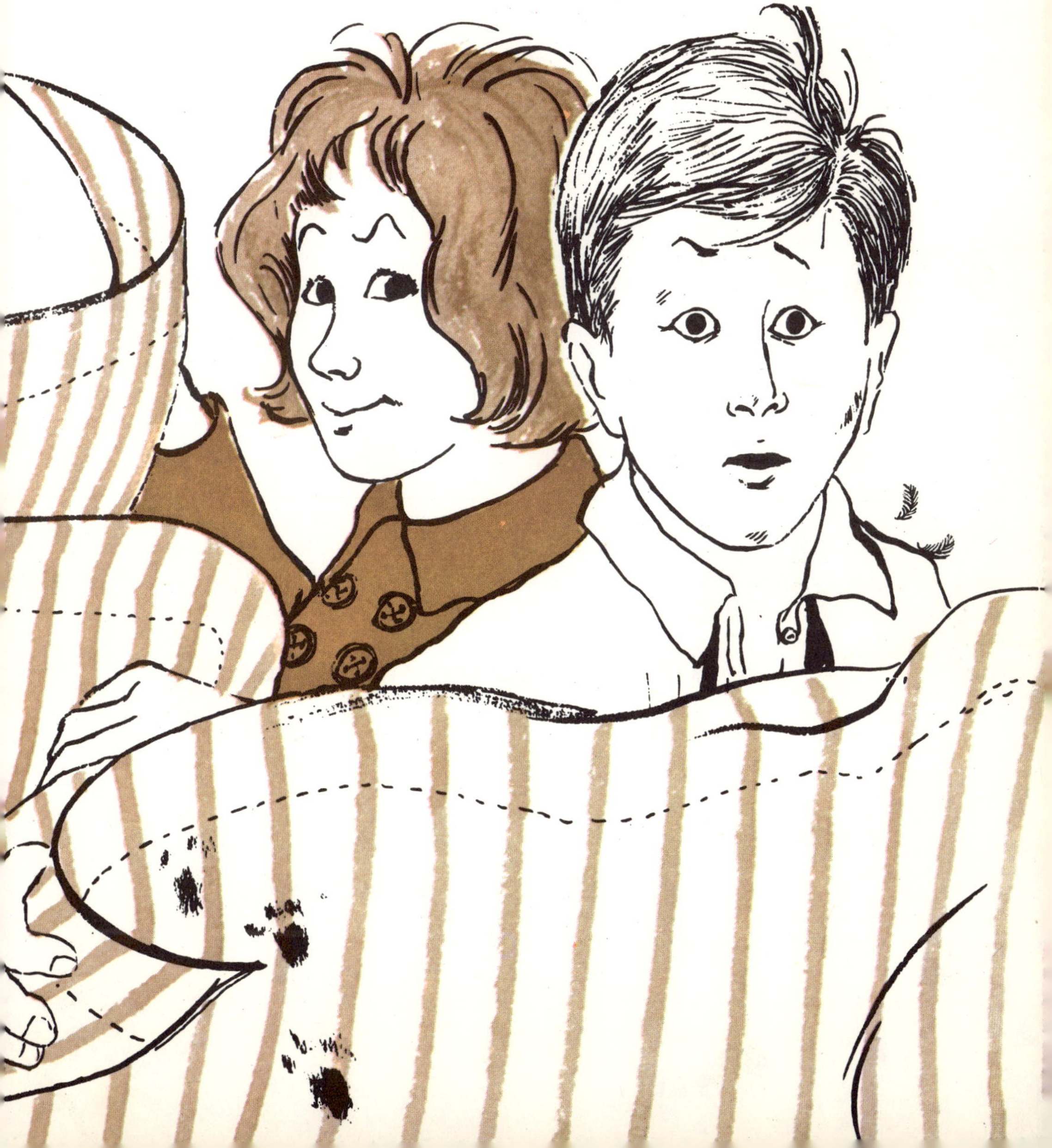

Thirty days later Mr. and Mrs. Wood and Michael drove out of the city.

"Well, here we go!" Mrs. Wood said, smiling.

"Um," Mr. Wood said. But by this time he was smiling, too.

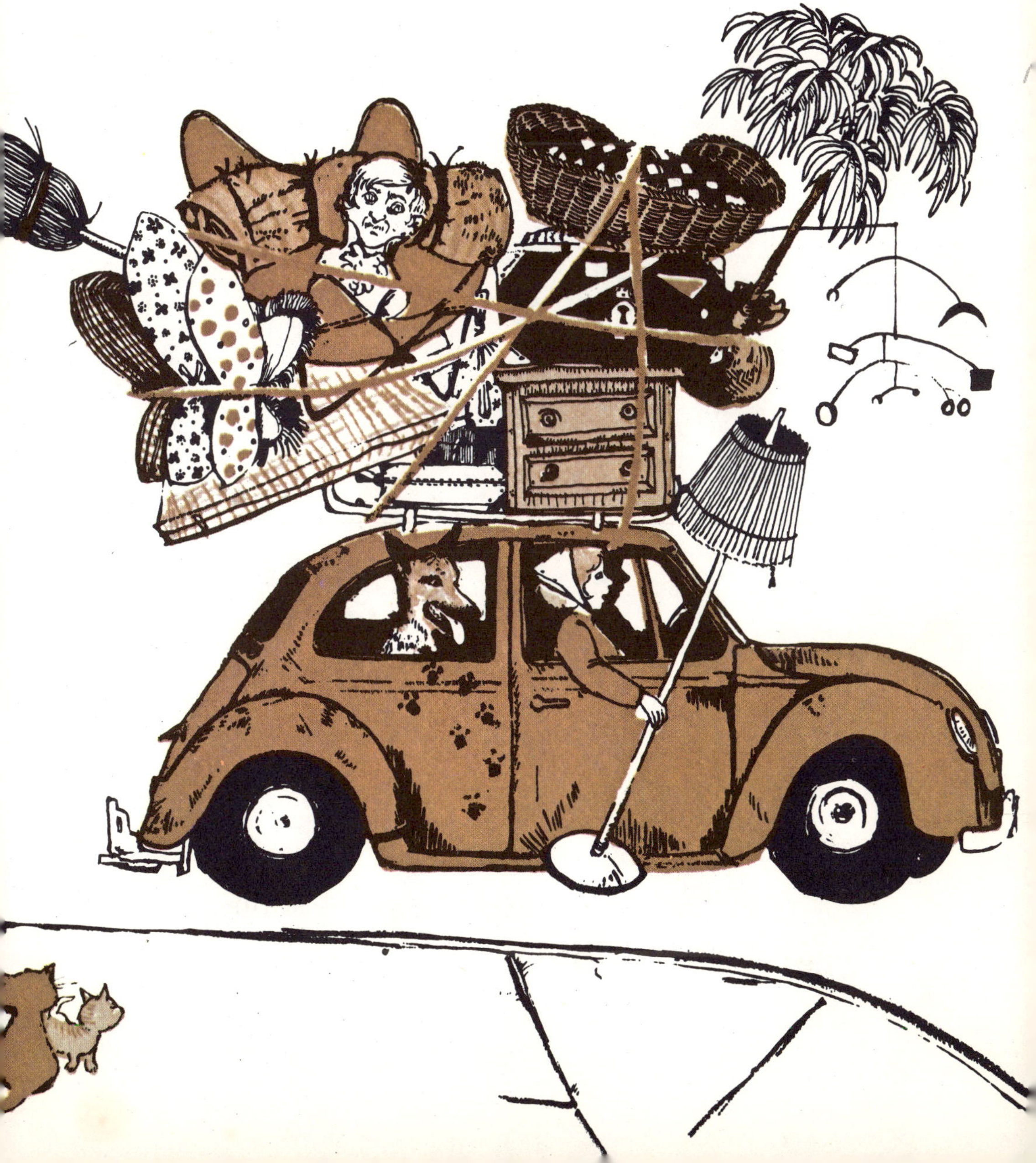

Michael hung out the car window, watching fields and woods and ponds flash by. His tail was wagging, his nose was busy sniffing new smells, and his eyes were no longer brown and sad but brown and eager.

THINKING IT OVER

Write your answers to these questions in your notebook or on a piece of paper. Remember to number your answers.

1. When did you first realize that this story couldn't really happen?
2. How did a ladder help Michael at the beginning of the story? How did a ladder cause trouble in the end?
3. Would you like to have owned Michael? If he had been a person, how would you describe him?
4. How would you describe Mrs. Quist? Have you ever known anyone like her?
5. Which two people wanted most to get rid of Michael? What reasons did each of them have? Were they good reasons?
6. Michael's friends had a good reason for nicknaming him "the upstairs dog." Can you think of any other nicknames to give Michael?

7. Do you think Michael will be happier in the country? Why or why not?

TALKING IT OVER

You may want to share your ideas about these questions with others who have read *Michael the Upstairs Dog.*

1. Do you think the dogs in this story acted more like dogs or more like people? Explain.
2. How did Michael communicate to the Woods that he was unhappy? How do you sometimes communicate without using words?
3. Was Michael a good pet? What do you think makes an animal a good pet?
4. How would you have acted if you had been Michael's master and returned home to find the mess the Woods found? Do you think Michael should have been punished?

5. How did the pictures help to make this a funny story? Do you think the story would have been funny without the pictures? Why or why not?
6. Have you ever been in a situation where things got entirely out of control as they did in this story? Tell what happened.
7. What can't you do where you live that you might be able to do if you lived somewhere else?

WHAT DID THE AUTHOR MEAN?

Here are some questions about words. Write your answers in your notebook or on a piece of paper. Remember to number your answers.

1. On page 39 the author said: "Some other dogs had found the laundry basket and were beginning a tug of war with Mrs. Wood's bathrobe." What did he mean by a *tug of war*? Have you ever had one?

2. Do you know what the word *avalanche* means? What is it usually used to describe? Why was this a good word to describe the dogs on page 42?
3. The author says on page 40: "The fight around the refrigerator and the tug of war turned into a general free-for-all." Can you tell what a *general free-for-all* might have been like?
4. The author said that Mr. and Mrs. Wood had a long discussion while they picked up and cleaned up everything. Mr. Wood did not have his newspaper to hide behind, so Mrs. Wood had the last word. Can you explain what the author meant by *the last word?*

ON YOUR OWN

1. Make a list of animals that would make good city pets. Tell why you think they're good choices.

2. Pretend that the ladder Mr. Wood built did not work. Can you think of a way for Michael to get from the apartment to the backyard? Draw a picture of your suggestion in your notebook.
3. When Michael was upset, he crawled into his thinking-place. Do you have a special place where you go to think? Would you like to write about it?
4. If you have a nickname, you might write a short history of it. Tell who gave it to you, why, and whether or not you like it. If you'd prefer a different one, tell what it is and why you'd prefer it.
5. Write a story of Michael's adventures in the country. This could be another book entitled *Michael the Country Dog*.

MY DOG
by Marchette Chute

His nose is short and scrubby;
   His ears hang rather low;
And he always brings the stick back,
   No matter how far you throw.

He gets spanked rather often
   For things he shouldn't do,
Like lying-on-beds, and barking,
   And eating up shoes when they're new.

He always wants to be going
   Where he isn't supposed to go.
He tracks up the house when it's snowing—
   Oh, puppy, I love you so.

Pretend you are Mrs. Wood and try to write a poem about Michael.

Copyright, 1932, renewal, ©, 1960 by Marchette Chute. From the book AROUND AND ABOUT by Marchette Chute. Published 1957 by E. P. Dutton & Co., Inc. and reprinted with their permission.

Is this the way you pictured the tug of war that Michael's friends had?

TUG OF WAR
by Kathleen Fraser

No one is quite sure
how to win at Tug of War
except that you pull
and pullll   and pulllllll
and just as you're sure
you are winning,
the other team pulls
and pulllls   and pulllllllls
and you fall their way
and then they fall your way
but
if everyone on your team
should suddenly take a big breath
and tug all together
with arms around each other
then you might just possibly win.

Copyright © 1968 by Kathleen Fraser. From STILTS, SOMERSAULTS, AND HEADSTANDS. Used by permission of Atheneum Publishers and Curtis Brown, Ltd.

COLLECTORS' ITEMS

SKI PUP
by Don Freeman

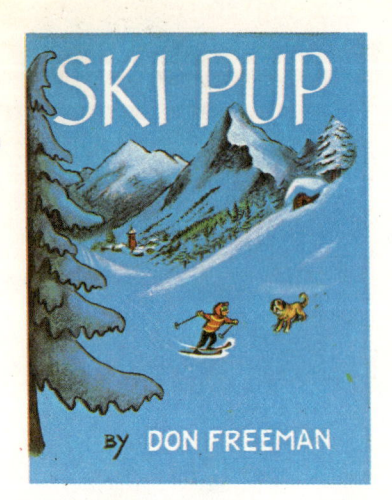

    Hugo was a Saint Bernard who was learning to be a rescue dog. One day there was a snowstorm, and Hugo found himself on skis. Read this story to find out how Hugo became a hero.

A THOUSAND LIGHTS AND FIREFLIES
by Alvin Tresselt

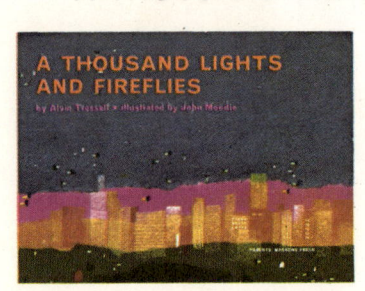

    The city and the country are very different. But they are also alike in many ways. Can you think of some ways in which they are the same?

THE TRUE BOOK OF DOGS
by Elsa Posell

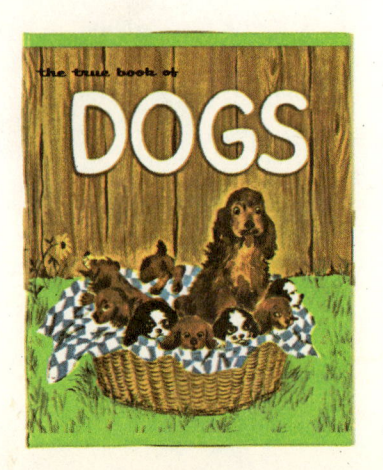

    This book will tell you how to train and care for a puppy. It will also teach you many things about different kinds of dogs.

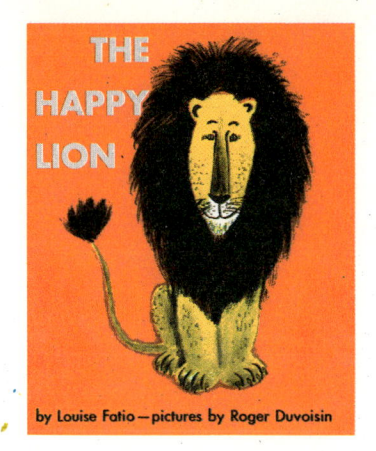

THE HAPPY LION
by Louise Fatio

The happy lion lived in the zoo. He had many friends who came to visit him. One day he took a walk into town. Do you think his friends were glad to see him?

PETER'S BROWNSTONE HOUSE
by Hila Colman

Peter lived with his great-grandfather in an old brownstone house. But Peter wanted to move to a new apartment building. One day a chance to move came. How could Grandpa possibly refuse?

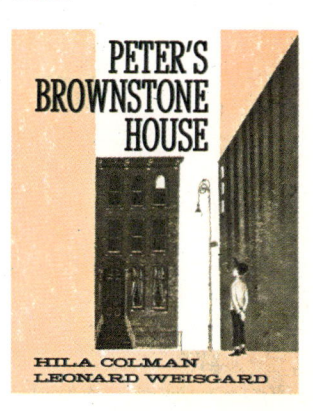

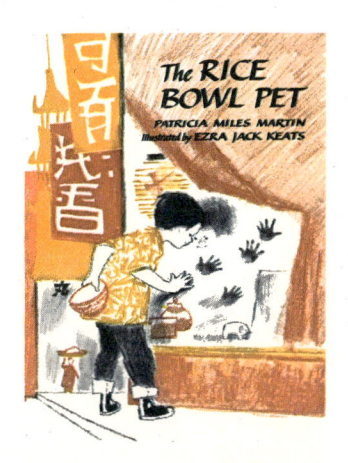

THE RICE BOWL PET
by Patricia Miles Martin

Ah Jim wanted a pet. But his family was big, and their apartment was small. He had to find a pet that was little enough to fit in a rice bowl. This is the story of Ah Jim's search through San Francisco for that pet.

SAMUEL F. BABBITT tells us that *The Forty-Ninth Magician* was really his wife's idea. She wanted a book to illustrate and thought that "The Forty-Ninth Magician" would make an interesting title for a story. Mr. Babbitt thought so, too, and he wrote the story that very night.

Since then, Mr. Babbitt has become the president of a college in Clinton, New York. Someday the Babbitts hope to do another story together. Perhaps it will have the same characters as this one.

THE FORTY-NINTH MAGICIAN

BY SAMUEL F BABBITT

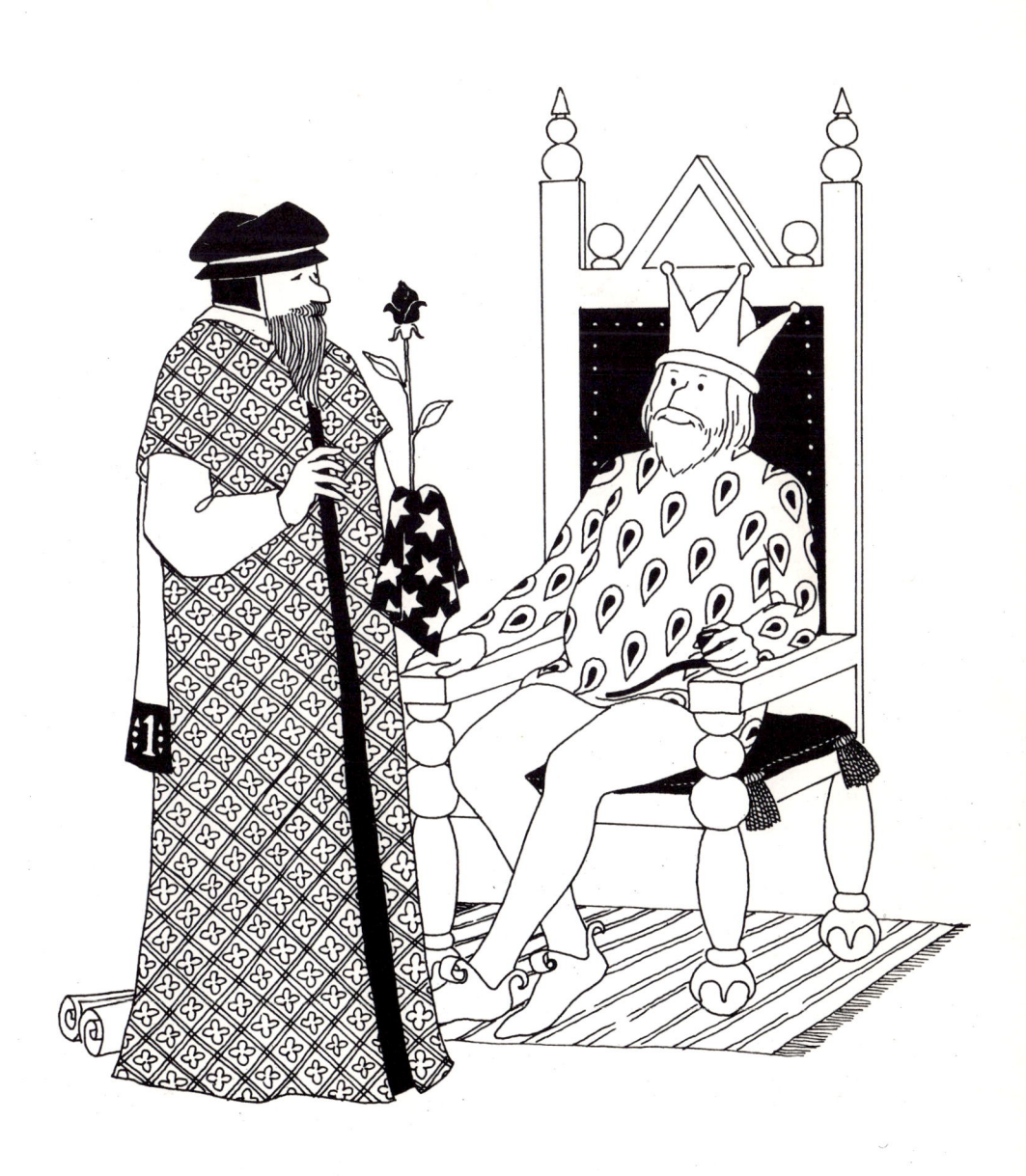

One magician is lots of fun.

Even two

or three at a time.

But forty-nine magicians all at once are very confusing

and not much fun at all.

Did you ever agree to do something that you later wished you hadn't? The king in this story finds himself in that predicament. As you read the story, think about whether you would have solved the problem in the way that the king did.

The Forty-Ninth Magician

by Samuel F. Babbitt
Pictures by Natalie Babbitt

Pantheon Books

For Chris, Tom, and Lucy

Copyright © 1966 by Samuel F. Babbitt
Illustrations: Copyright © 1966 by Natalie M. Babbitt
Reprinted by permission of Random House, Inc.
And Brockhampton Press Limited

It all started when the king was very small and there was only one magician at the court. He was an old magician and a very good friend to the king.

In fact, the young king loved his magician, and one day, after he had performed an especially difficult trick, the king said that he would take care of the sons of the magician and *their* sons for as long as they wanted to live in his castle.

The king didn't know that the magician had seven sons until they came to live in the castle the very next day.

What is more, they were all magicians!

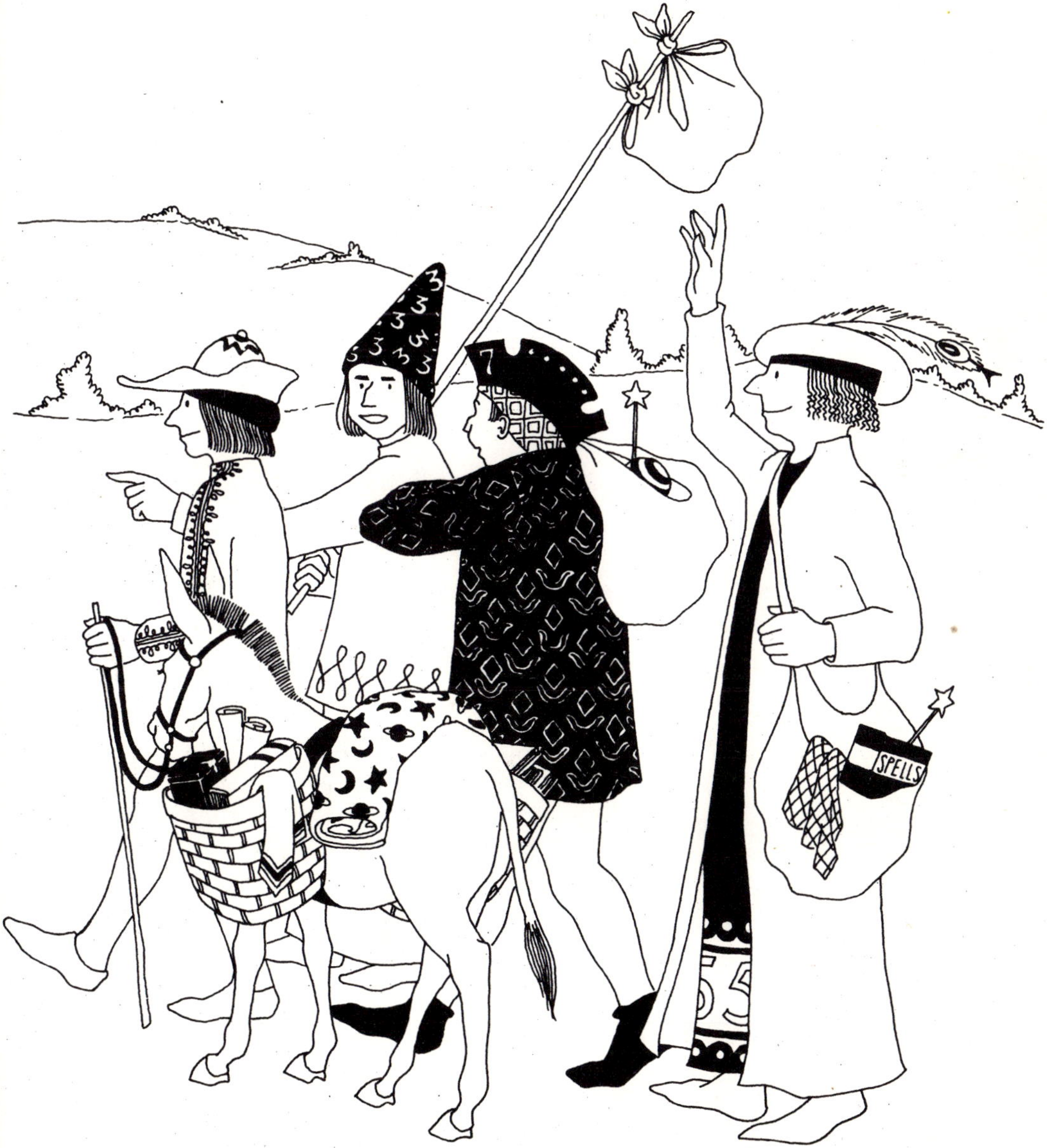
SPELLS

At first it was great fun. Each day the king would clap his hands to have a different magician perform for him in the Great Hall.

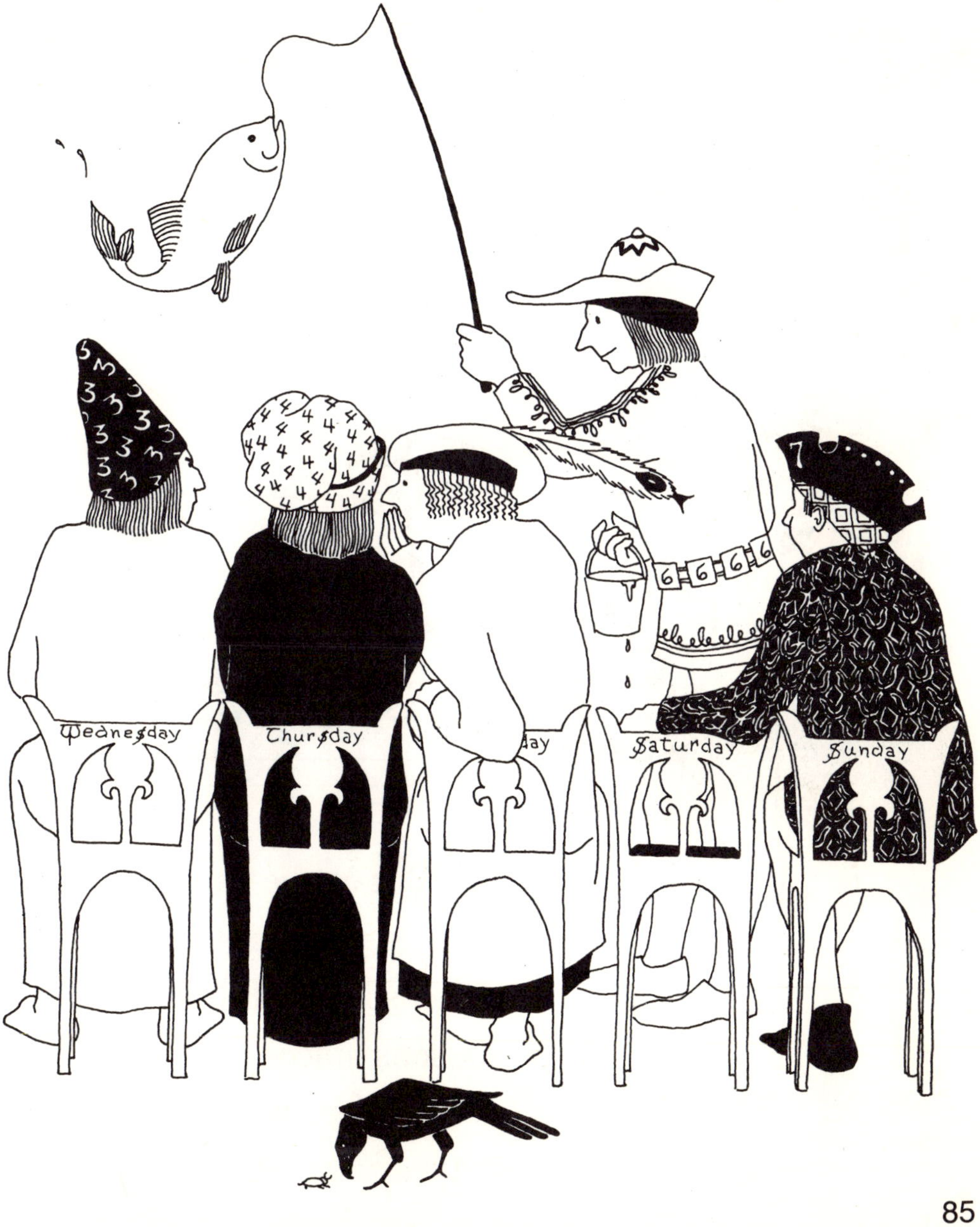
Wednesday
Thursday
Saturday
Sunday

But as the young king grew older, those seven sons each had six sons apiece. At last there were forty-nine in all.

Forty-nine magicians!

Since there were now seven magicians for each day in the week, the king had to have his workmen build a special stage to hold them.

Friday
Friday
Friday
Friday
Friday
Friday
Friday
Saturday
Saturday
Saturday
Saturday
Saturday
Saturday
Saturday
Sunday
Sunday
Sunday
Sunday
Sunday
Sunday
Sunday

And the forty-nine magicians began to compete with each other to please the king and all the people. They had to do a lot of practicing to keep up.

It got so bad after a while that the king couldn't find a place to take a nap because all the rooms in the castle were being used by magicians practicing their new tricks.

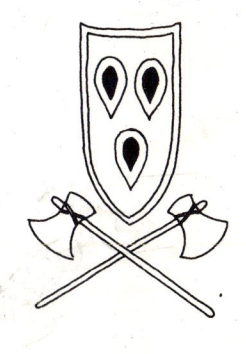

Finally, one day at lunch, someone turned a visiting ambassador's wine cup into a toad.

"STOP!" said the king. (He was feeling rather cross because he had missed his nap again.) "Forty-nine magicians," said the king in a loud voice, "are forty-eight too many."

So he called in a passing wise man and asked how to choose one from the forty-nine to be the King's Own Magician.

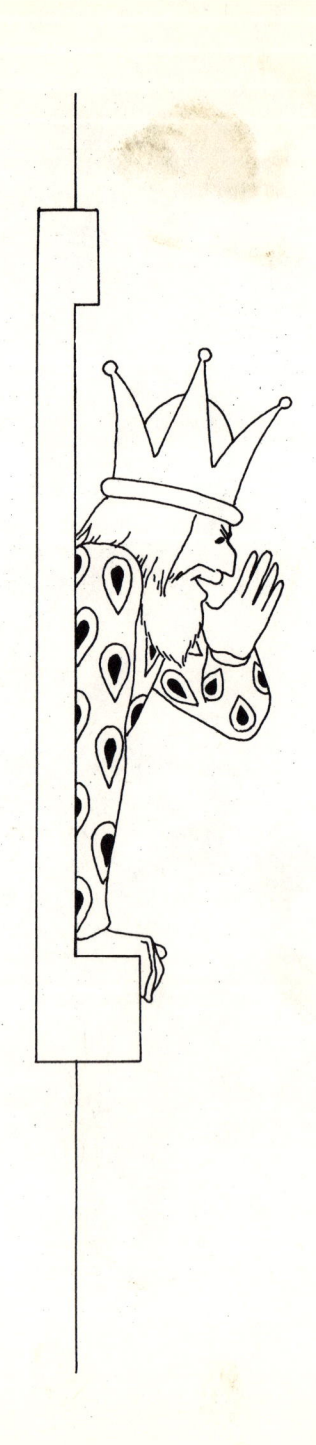

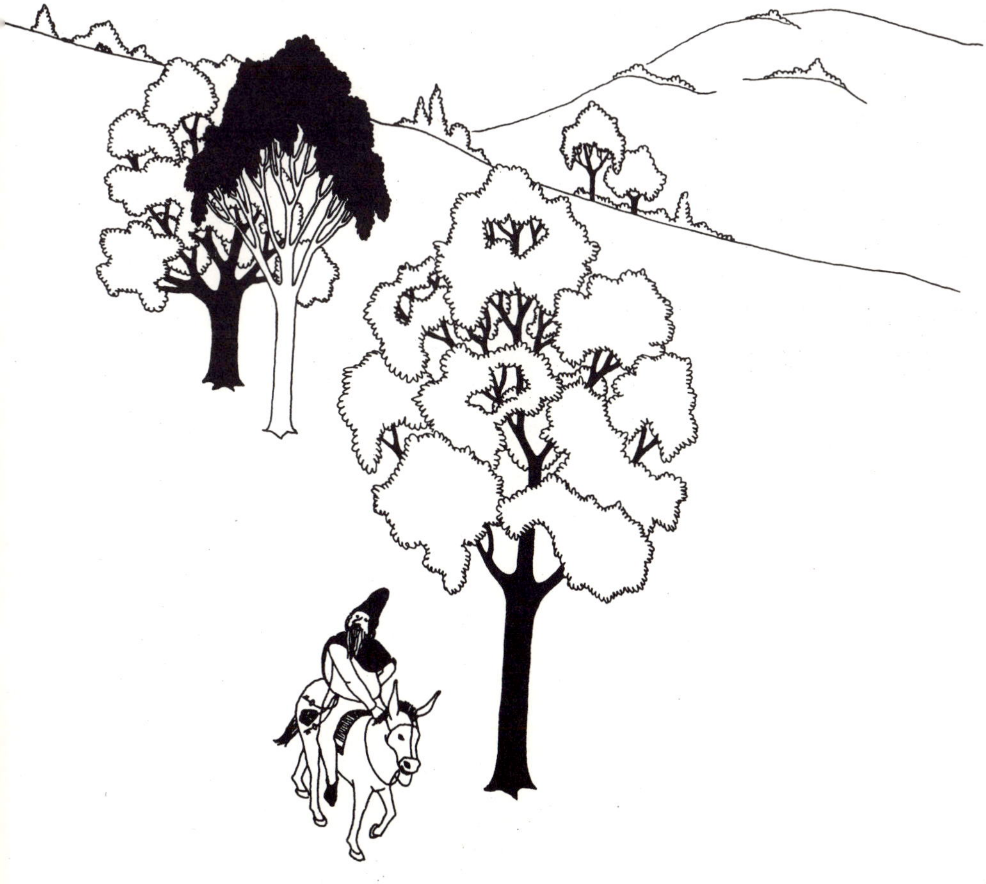

The wise man thought for a moment . . .

and then said there was only one solution.

He whispered in the royal ear,

gave the king his bill,

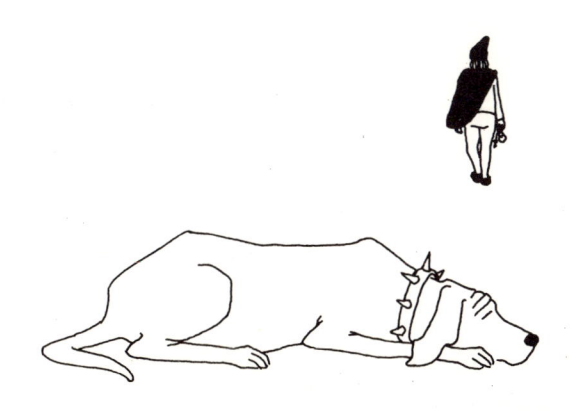

and went on his way again.

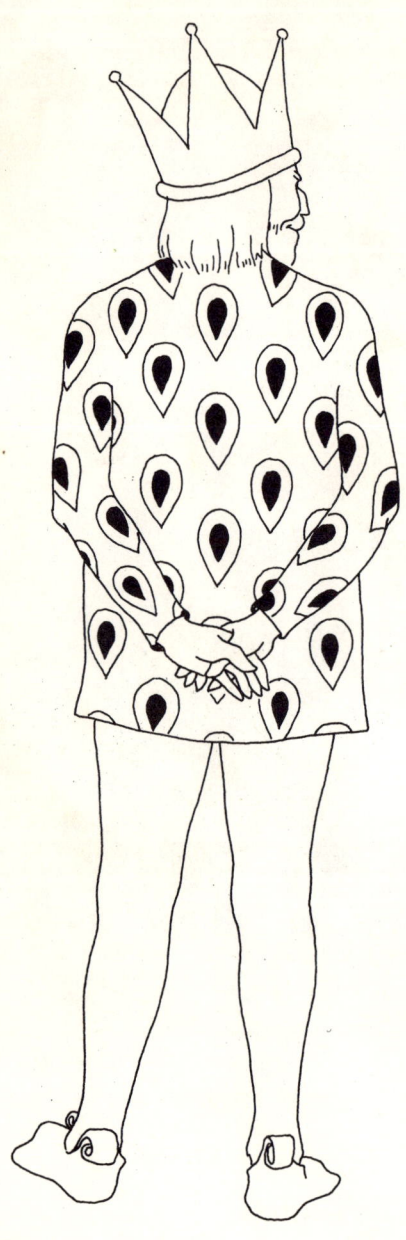

That night, following the wise man's suggestion, the king had it announced that there would be a special contest for all the magicians a week from Friday in the Great Hall. The one who did the best magic would be the King's Own Magician. The others would simply have to go and find other castles to perform in.

Well, you know the king didn't get any naps *that* week.

In all the confusion of preparation and practice, the thirty-ninth magician caught his own glance in a mirror which his cousin was holding

and turned himself
into a spider.

On the day of the contest, people from near and far gathered in the Great Hall to watch.

The magicians came in with their equipment—everything they needed to perform their best tricks.

When the king clapped his hands, the first magician stepped up onto the platform.

It was *quite* a trick.

As the day went by, each magician

tried to do better than
the one before.

Finally the forty-ninth magician came to the platform. He didn't have any boxes or mirrors. He didn't have any helpers or animals.

Just himself.

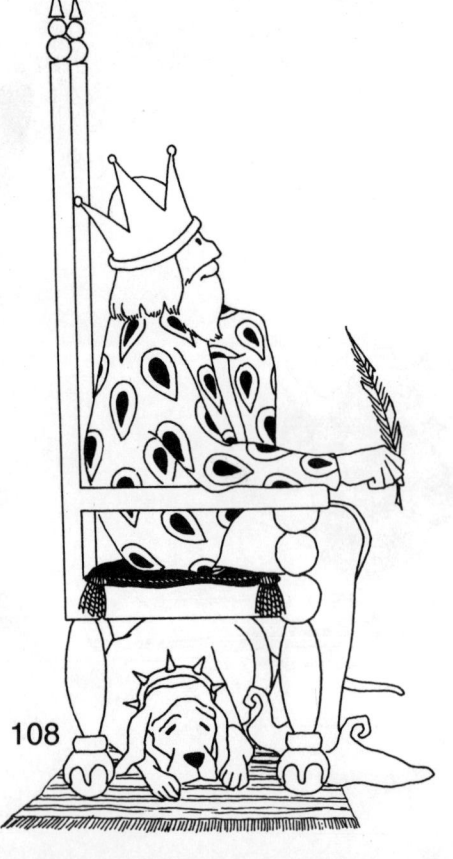

He looked at the king and he said, "Sire, you have seen wonderful things today, but if you come outside with me, I'll show you how to make hours into minutes and minutes into seconds until time itself disappears."

The king smiled, for he knew that time is time, and you can't make a minute out of an hour—not even with mirrors. But he was a fair-minded king, so he got up and followed the young man out of the castle. Besides, it felt good to stretch his legs.

In a broad field nearby, the forty-ninth magician showed the king how to make a squeaking whistle by holding a blade of grass between his thumbs and blowing through them.

At a stream they built a wheel of reeds that spun as the water rushed by.

Then they began to make a dam in the stream so that cool water collected and formed a little pool.

They were still at it when a messenger came from the castle to tell them it was time for supper. The messenger was very surprised to see the king in the water.

Looking up, the king suddenly realized that, just as the young magician had promised, the hours had become minutes, and the minutes had seemed like seconds on that magic afternoon.

As they walked home through the cool places under the great trees, the king was smiling.

"We'll come back
and do some more
of that tomorrow,"
he said.

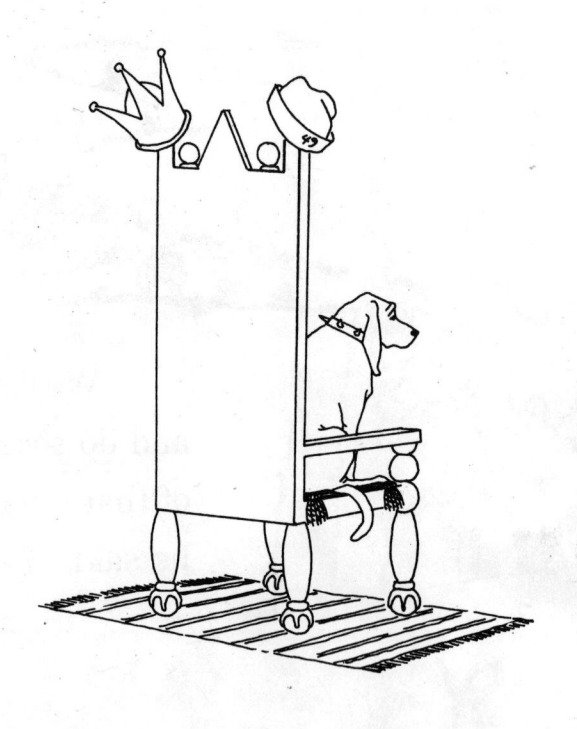

And so it was that the forty-ninth magician became the First Magician of the Land—and a very good friend to the king.

THINKING IT OVER

Write your answers to these questions in your notebook or on a piece of paper. Remember to number your answers.

1. How was the beginning of this book different from the way books usually begin?
2. The king is a little boy when the story begins. Why didn't the author begin the story with a grown-up king, as shown in the opening pages?
3. The story mentions that with so many magicians around, the king couldn't even find a place to take a nap. What other problems can you think of that forty-nine magicians might have made?
4. Do you think the wise man's idea to have a contest was a good one? Can you think of any other way in which the king might have solved his problem?
5. The forty-ninth magician said, ". . . I'll

show you how to make hours into minutes and minutes into seconds until time itself disappears." What did he mean? What did he really show the king? Is there something you enjoy doing that makes hours into minutes and minutes into seconds?

6. Why do you suppose the king had never discovered the wonders and beauties of nature?

TALKING IT OVER

You may want to share your ideas about these questions with others who have read *The Forty-Ninth Magician.*

1. There are two kinds of magic in this story. First, there is the magic of the forty-eight magicians. What kinds of things could these magicians do? How would you define this kind of magic? Second, there is the magic of the

forty-ninth magician. In what way is this a different kind of magic? How would you define this kind of magic?

2. If you were the king, would you have named the forty-ninth magician the First Magician of the Land? If you would have chosen one of the others, tell why.

3. If you were a king, would you want a magician in your court? Why?

4. What makes magic so interesting? Why do people like magic? What must a good magician be able to do?

5. Poets and storytellers have written of magical moments spent in the out-of-doors. Have you enjoyed any times playing outside that you would call magical?

6. Which do you think made the king happier: having a First Magician or having a very good friend? Why? Which would you rather have?

7. What did you learn from the story about

the kingdom over which the king ruled? Do you think he was a good king? Explain why you think as you do.
8. Although the story is about a king who has too many magicians, the author seems to be trying to tell his readers something far more important. Can you think what it is?

TAKING A LOOK AT ART

1. The author never mentions the king's dog in the story. But the artist has given us some ideas about what the dog is like. What did you find out about it from the pictures?
2. Each picture the artist has drawn for the story offers many things to look at. Did you notice the tiny egg from which the magician produced the peacock on page 80? Did you see the way in which the artist identified magicians by number on

certain pages? Make a list of some other details you found in pictures that some of the others reading the story might not have noticed. You might exchange lists later to see if there were any you missed.

3. The last line of the story tells us that the forty-ninth magician became a very good friend to the king. How has the artist shown us through her picture that this is true?

*Almost everyone has a friend like Joe.
After reading this poem, think about what
you've learned from someone like him.*

DISCOVERY
by Harry Behn

In a puddle left from last week's rain,
   A friend of mine whose name is Joe
   Caught a tadpole, and showed me where
   Its froggy legs were beginning to grow.

Then we turned over a musty log,
   With lichens on it in a row,
   And found some fiddleheads of ferns
   Uncoiling out of the moss below.

We hunted around, and saw the first
   Jack-in-the-pulpits beginning to show,
   And even discovered under a rock
   Where spotted salamanders go.

   I learned all this one morning from Joe,
   But how much more there is to know!

From THE GOLDEN HIVE, © 1957, 1962, 1966, by Harry Behn. Reprinted by permission of Harcourt, Brace & World, Inc. and Curtis Brown, Ltd.

*The writer tells his feelings about nature.
Do you think the king felt this way when he
first discovered the beautiful outdoors?*

When spring comes
I feel like a
Daisy just opening up into a new life.
I feel like running twenty miles
And taking off my heavy coat
And putting on a pair of sneakers.
I feel like I started a new life
And everything is better
Than it was before.
I get faster
In running and I can go swimming outdoors.
It feels like the smell of new flowers
And the animals
Coming up from their holes,
The birds coming back from their vacations.
I love spring.

by Michael Patrick, age 10

"When spring comes" by Michael Patrick from MIRACLES: POEMS BY CHILDREN OF THE ENGLISH-SPEAKING WORLD, collected by Richard Lewis. Copyright © 1966 by Richard Lewis. Reprinted by permission of Simon & Schuster Inc. and Penguin Books Ltd.

COLLECTORS' ITEMS

THE HOLE IN THE TREE
by Jean George

Paula and Scot watch a hole in their tree grow and change with each new tenant. Perhaps the king and the forty-ninth magician watched this same kind of magic on their outings together.

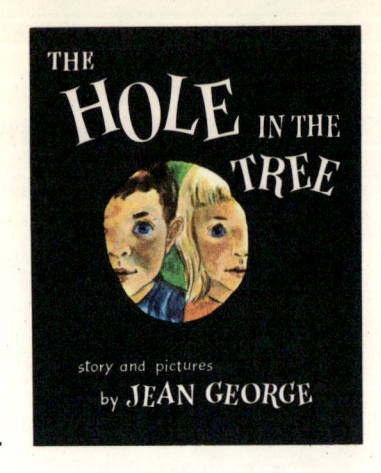

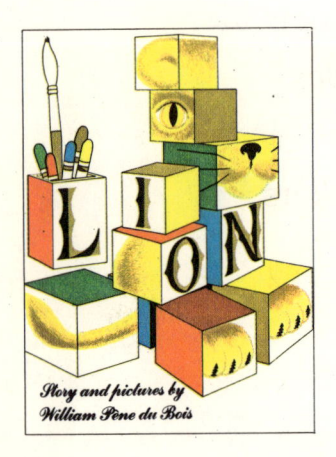

LION
by William Pène du Bois

Foreman was drawing the very first lion ever to be seen. He made a small, brightly colored animal with feathers and fur and fish scales. Then he stepped back and wondered. Was this really how a lion should look?

TWO HUNDRED RABBITS
by Lonzo Anderson

It was Festival Day at the castle. The boy wanted so much to entertain the king and win a job in his court. But what could he do that no one else had ever done?

DO TIGERS EVER BITE KINGS?
by Barbara Wersba

The queen was excited. She had never been on a tiger hunt before. But the king was worried. He wondered, "Do tigers ever bite kings?"

HENRY HUGGINS
by Beverly Cleary

Henry had just about decided that nothing exciting was ever going to happen to him when along came this stray, hungry dog. The year that followed brought many adventures.

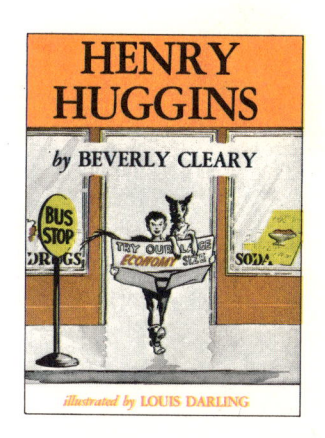

HOW TO BE A NATURE DETECTIVE
by Millicent Selsam

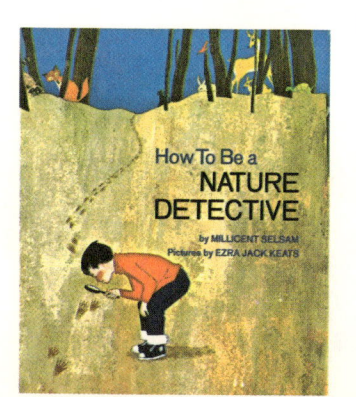

A nature detective learns to look and listen. He can find clues almost anywhere. This book will help you become a private eye in the world of nature.

BRINTON TURKLE says that Obadiah the Bold was born on a valentine. Mr. Turkle made the valentine for the daughter of a friend of his. On the card he drew a shy, red-headed Quaker boy. ". . . from the beginning he looked as if he deserved a name and a story," says the author.

At first, Obadiah was going to be a Philadelphian. But after a trip to Nantucket Island, Mr. Turkle decided that he must have lived there.

Another story about Obadiah is now being written.

Brinton Turkle

OBADIAH THE BOLD

OBADIAH

NEW YORK · THE VIKING PRESS

In this story, Obadiah Starbuck receives a very special birthday present. The present helps him decide what he will be when he grows up. But sometimes even young boys change their minds.

the BOLD

STORY AND PICTURES BY

Brinton Turkle

From OBADIAH THE BOLD
Written and illustrated by Brinton Turkle
Copyright © 1965 by Brinton Turkle. All rights reserved
Reprinted by permission of The Viking Press, Inc.

This is Obadiah Starbuck. He is running home with his new spyglass. It is made of brass, and it is very beautiful.

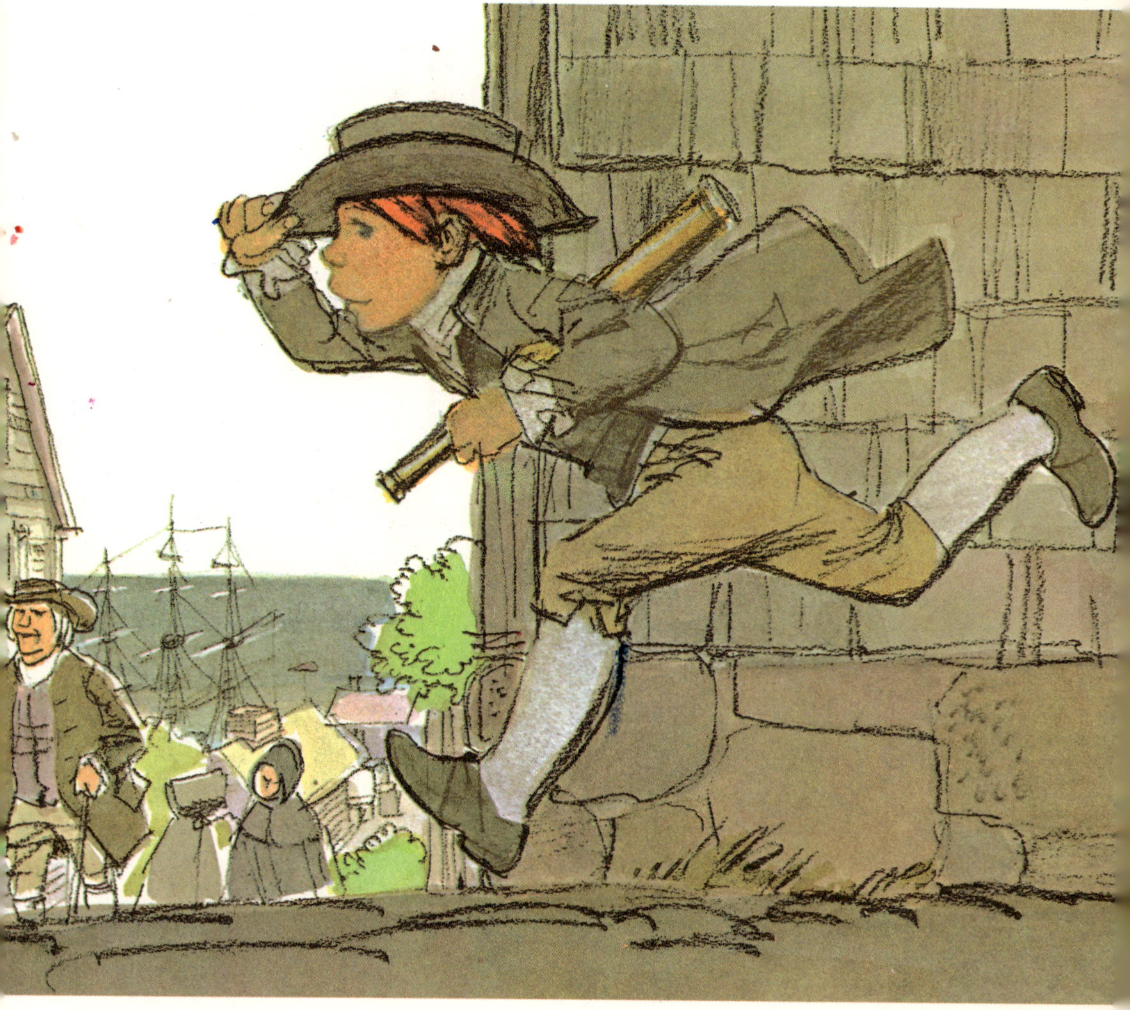

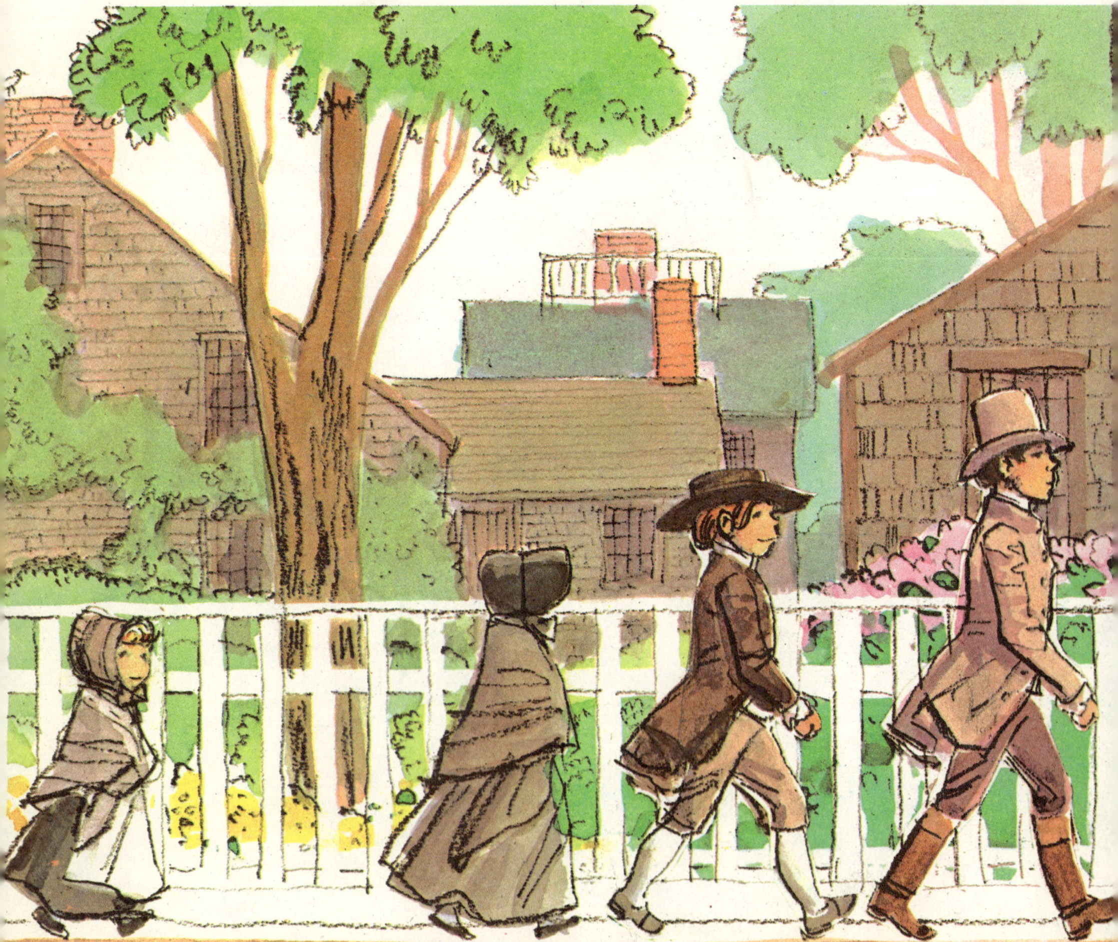

The rest of his family, all dressed in their best clothes, are going to Friends Meeting:[1] Father, Mother, Moses, Asa, Rebecca, and Rachel. Obadiah comes between Rebecca and Rachel. The beautiful new spyglass was a birthday present. When Obadiah tried to take it to Meeting, Father said, "No," and Obadiah had to run back home with it.

1. **Friends Meeting** a meeting for worship by a Christian group called the Society of Friends.

On First Day,[1] all the Quakers[2] on Nantucket Island[3] go to Meeting. There the men sit on one side, and the women sit on the other. When Obadiah arrived, Meeting had already begun. He sat on a wooden bench with the men.

Meeting for Worship was long and quiet. Sometimes a Friend would stand up and recite verses from the Bible or talk about God. Obadiah tried to think about God, but it was easier to think about his shiny new spyglass. A fly buzzed on the sunny windowpane. All of a sudden, Obadiah knew what he wanted to be when he grew up.

---

1. **First Day** Sunday.
2. **Quakers** another name for Friends.
3. **Nantucket Island** island off the coast of Massachusetts.

135

He wanted to be a pirate. He wanted to be a fearless pirate who roamed the seas and had chests of treasure buried in secret places. Obadiah Starbuck, Terror of the Seven Seas!
OBADIAH THE BOLD!

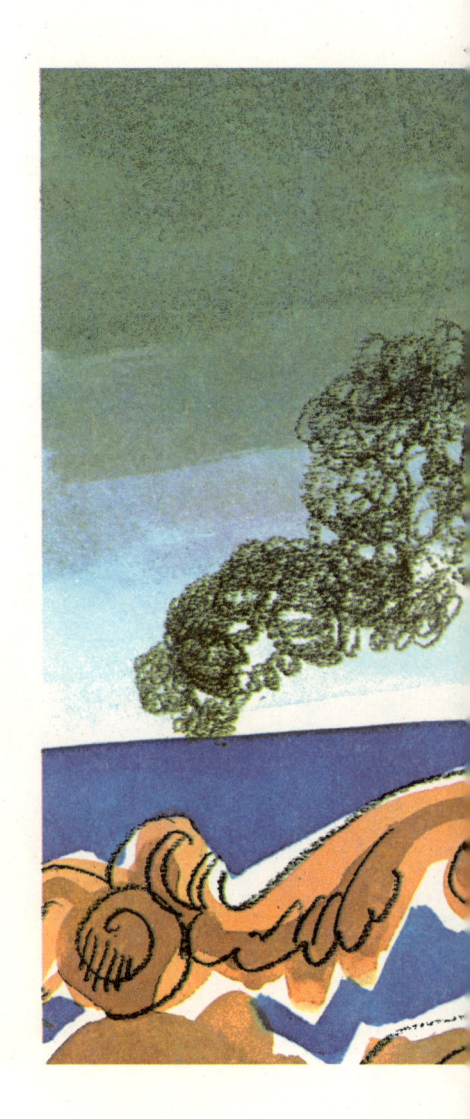

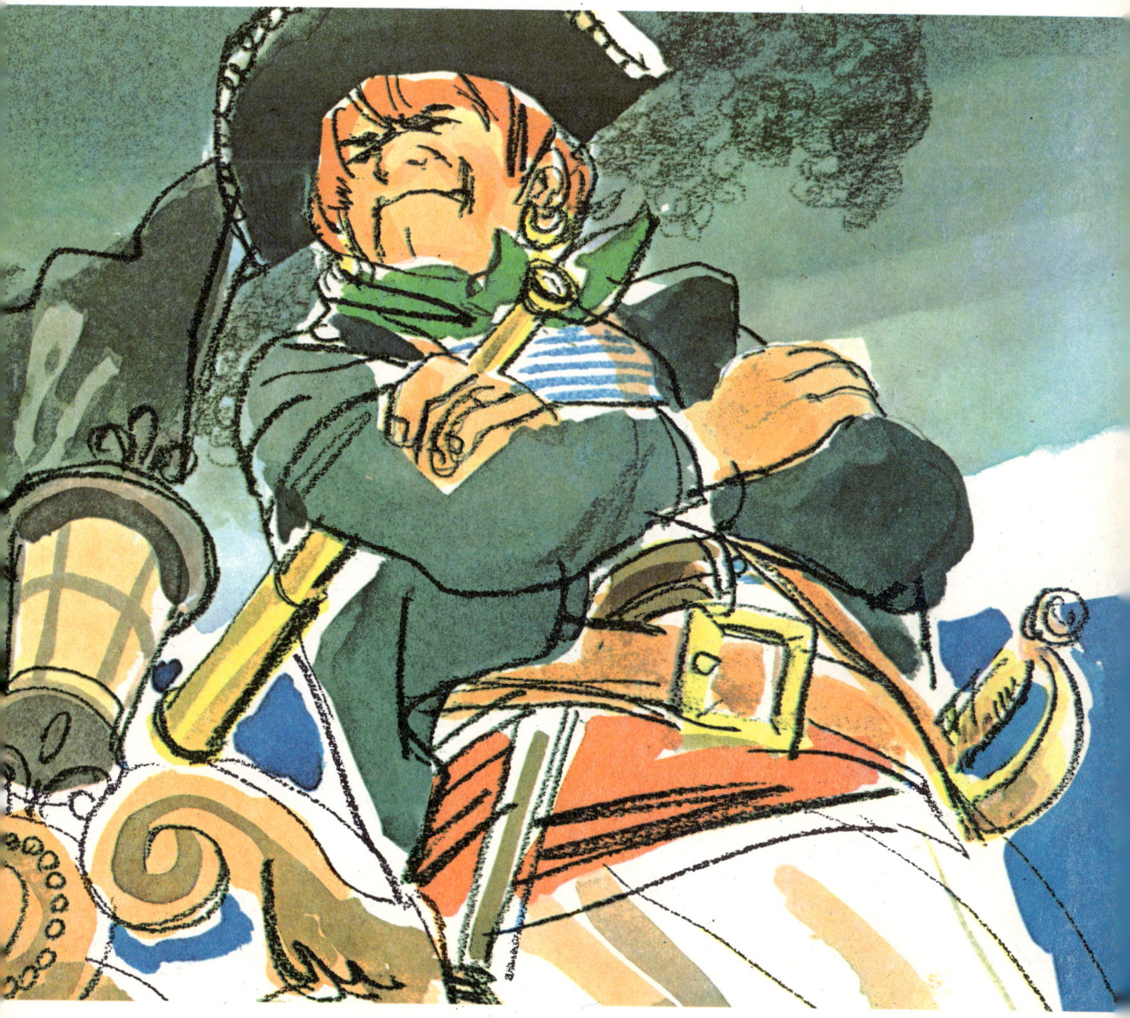

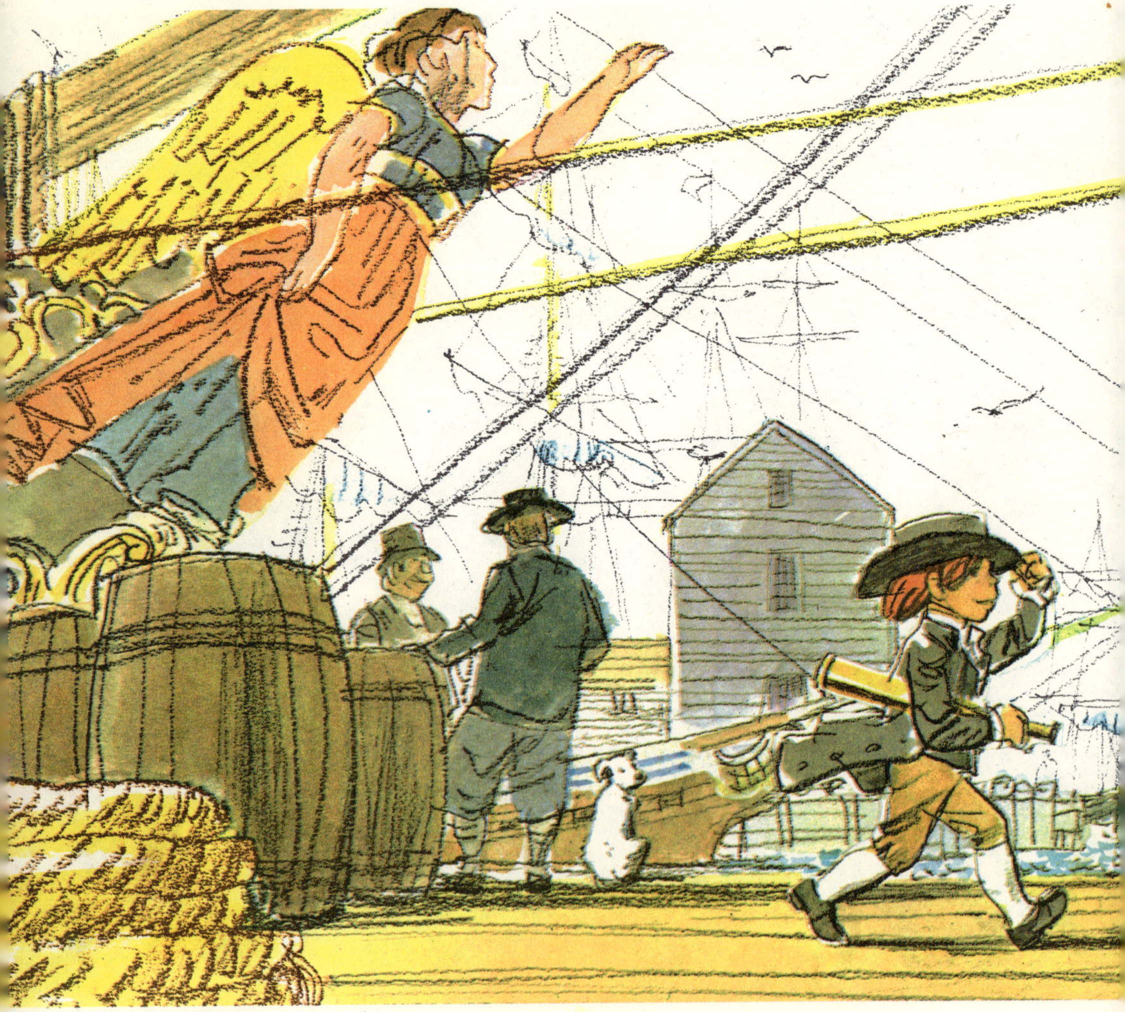

If Obadiah's new spyglass couldn't go to Meeting, it went every place else with him: to the wharf, to bed, and even to the table at mealtimes.

"When I grow up, I'm going to be a pirate," he said at suppertime.

Moses whooped. "Has thee[1] ever heard of a Quaker pirate?" he asked Asa.

"Perhaps he could be a Friendly pirate," said Mother. Everyone laughed.

Father said, "I don't think a Starbuck has ever been a pirate, Obadiah; but if that is thy[2] heart's desire, I hope thee will be a good one."

---

1. **thee** you.
2. **thy** your.

One rainy day Rachel asked him to play house with her.

"No!" Obadiah snorted. "I am too big to play house with thee."

In the parlor Moses and Asa had just filled the woodbox. Rebecca was sweeping the hearth.[1]

"Let's play pirate," Obadiah suggested.

---

1. **hearth** floor of a fireplace.

141

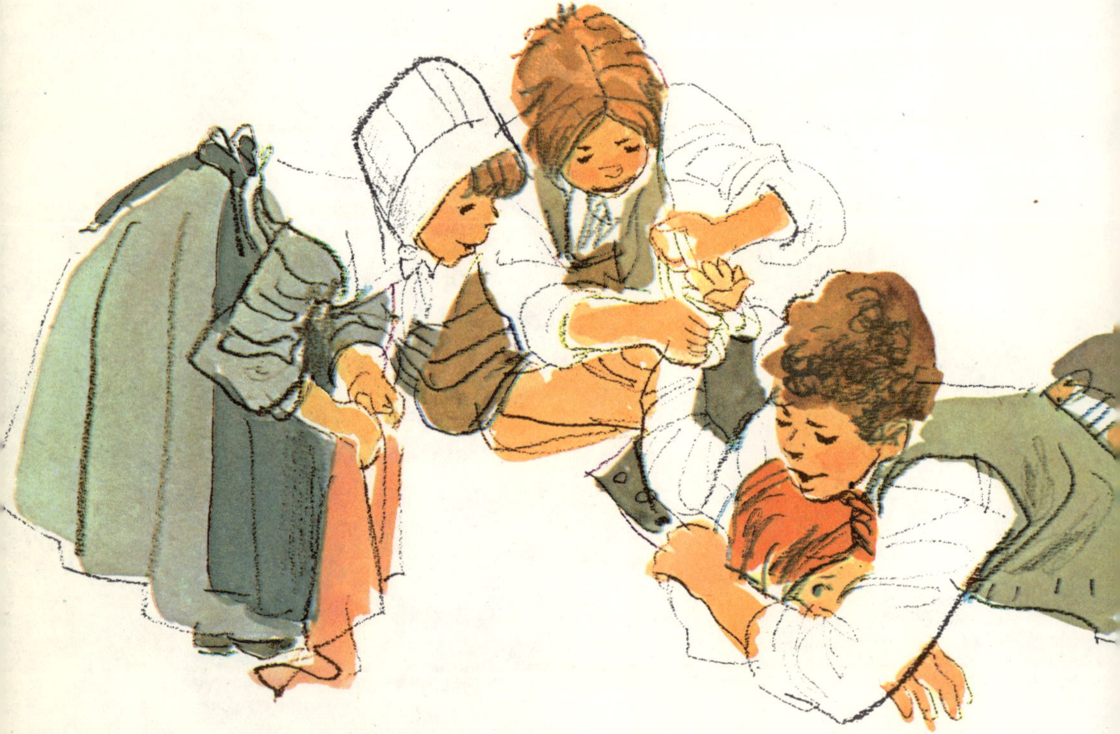

"All right," said Asa. "First, Moses and I capture thee!" They were bigger than he was, and there were two of them. Rebecca got some rope and a piece of cloth. Obadiah was tied and blindfolded.

"We're putting thee in the brig,"[1] they said.

---
1. **brig** jail on a warship.

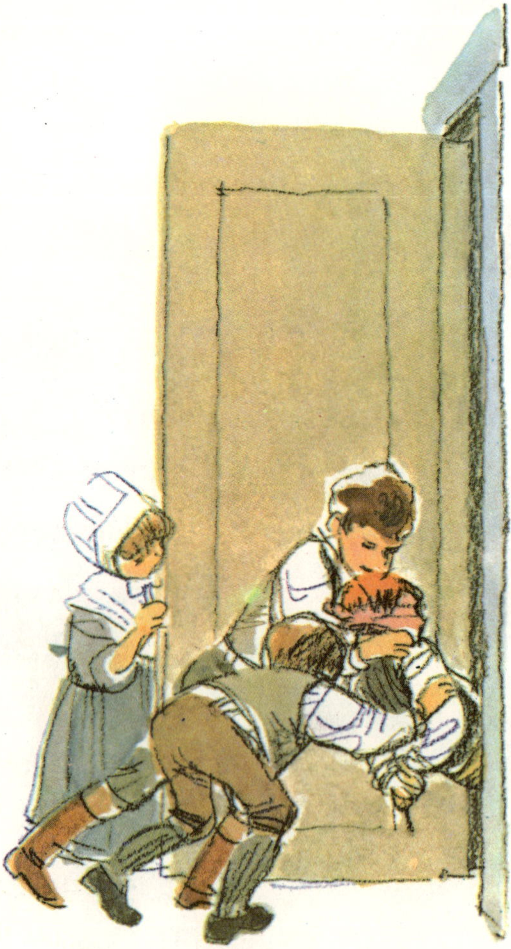

"That's not the way to play pirate!" shouted Obadiah.

"It is, too!" they said. They put him in the broom closet and shut the door.

Pirates are brave and don't cry. But Obadiah was frightened and wanted very much to cry. He tried to push his way out of the closet, but someone was holding the door.

"Avast[1] there, mate![2] Shall we keelhaul[3] this dog, or hang him from the yardarm?"[4]

That didn't sound like Moses.

"No, we'll send him down to Davy Jones.[5] Get out the plank."

That didn't sound like Asa.

---

1. **avast** stop.
2. **mate** an officer on a ship.
3. **keelhaul** punish.
4. **yardarm** either end of a beam that supports a square sail.
5. **Davy Jones** the spirit of the sea.

There was a scuffling sound, and at last the door was opened. He was pushed and shoved until he was standing unsteadily on some kind of board.

"March!" someone said.

He didn't budge.

"Jab him with a harpoon!"[1]

Something poked him in the ribs, and he had to jump.

---

1. **harpoon** spear used for hunting whales.

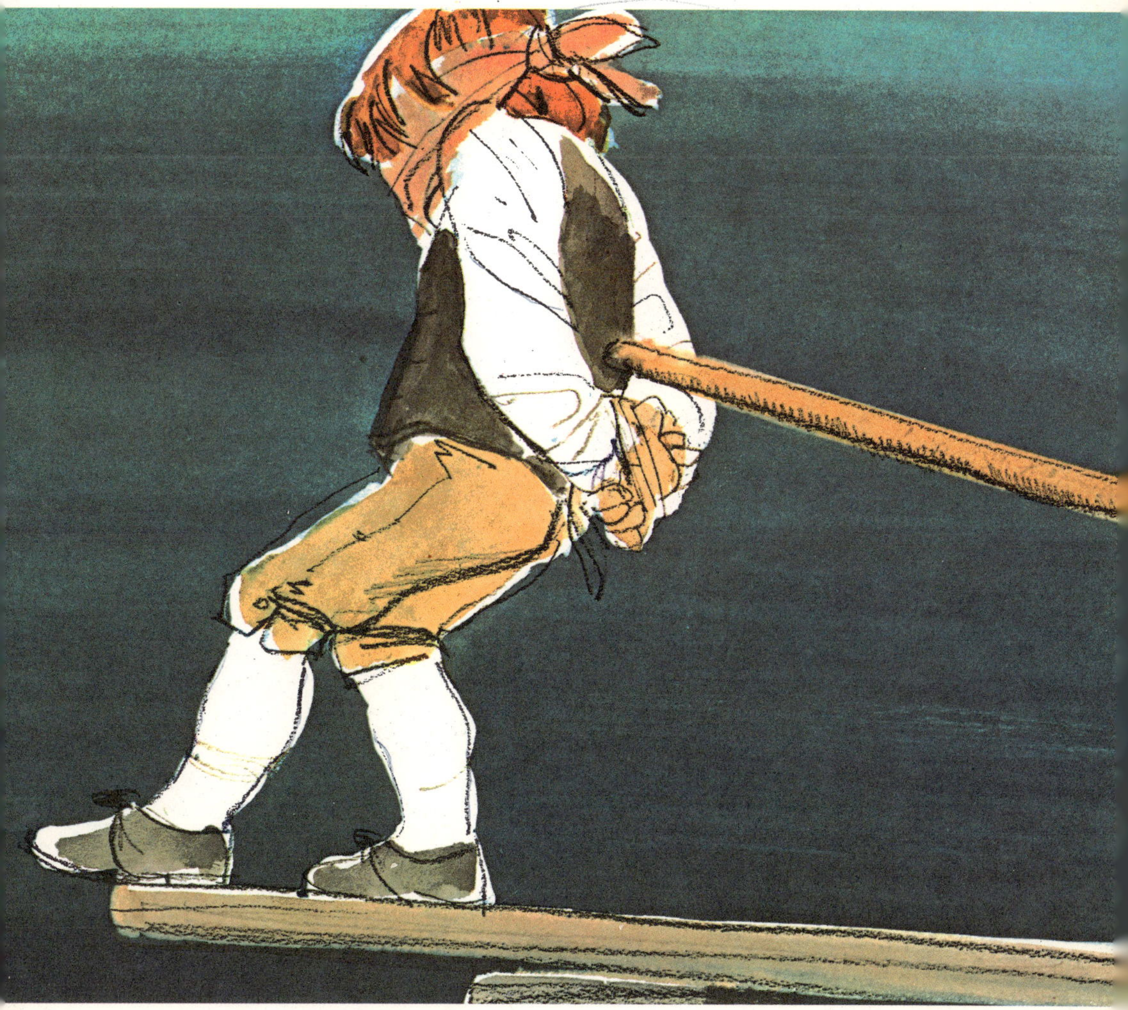

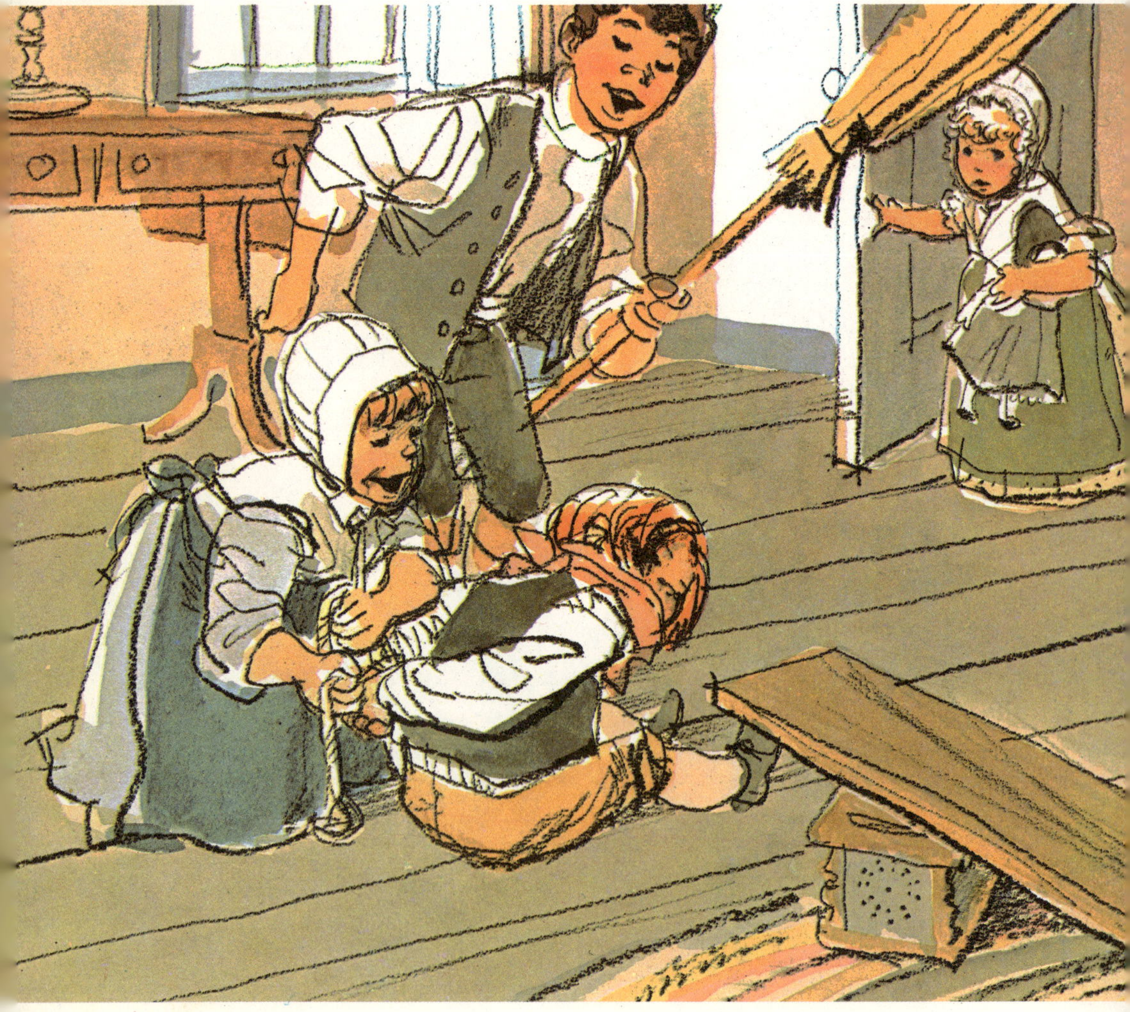

He was surprised to find himself on the floor. Rebecca took off the blindfold and untied him. The plank was only a board from the woodshed. The harpoon must have been the broom handle.

Moses and Asa were laughing. Obadiah didn't think it was funny.

The rest of the afternoon, he played house with Rachel.

That night he didn't take his spyglass to the supper table. He didn't even take it to bed with him.

The next day Obadiah walked back and forth three times in front of Father's study before Father looked up from the letter he was writing and said, "Come in, Son."

Obadiah stood stiffly beside the desk and didn't know how to begin.

"Is anything troubling thee?" Father asked.

"Father, is it true that pirates have to walk the plank?"[1]

"Why, yes, if they're caught."

"And must they hang from the yardarm?"

"If they're wicked enough."

"Then . . . then I don't want to be a pirate, no matter how brave they are."

Father sat Obadiah on his knee.

---

1. **walk the plank** walk off a ship's plank into deep water.

"Pirates aren't really very brave, Obadiah," he said. "I never heard of a pirate as brave as thy own grandfather."

"What did he do?"

"He sailed around the Horn four times."

"What's the Horn, Father?"

"Cape Horn is land's end at the very tip of South America. Thee has to go around it to get to the China Seas, and it is very dangerous."

"Why?"

"Because there are rocks and ice and foul weather. Terrible storms blow down there. Twice thy grandfather was almost shipwrecked, but he brought his ship through and never lost a man. He was such a brave sailor that his men gave him a fine gift."

"What was it?"

"I'll show it to thee." Father went over to the high chest in the corner. From the top drawer, he brought out a red box which he opened. Inside was the most beautiful thing Obadiah had ever seen.

"A watch!"

"It's like a watch, Son, but it's especially for sailors. It's called a *chronometer*. It keeps very accurate time, and that helps to tell exactly where thy ship is at sea. Pick it up and look at it."

Obadiah picked it up with great care.

Father said, "Turn it over and look on the back."

There was writing on the back. Obadiah couldn't read the letters very well, but one word almost jumped out at him.

"OBADIAH!" he yelled. "It's my name!"

Father took the chronometer and held it up to the window where it twinkled, crystal and gold in the light. "For Obadiah Starbuck," he read. "Brave Captain of the ship *Bonaventure* from the ship's company. 1798."

"That's my name!"

"Thee was named for thy grandfather, Obadiah. I think he would want thee to have this timepiece when thee is a man. I'll put it away for now." Father returned it to the drawer. "It's a fine day, Son. Get thy spyglass, and come up to the roof with me."

It *was* a fine day. In Nantucket harbor a whaling ship was rolling at anchor as if she wanted to get under way. Beyond the breakwater[1] a ship was headed for Boston.

"Which way is the Horn, Father?"

"Away off yonder," Father said, pointing.

"Farther than France?"

"Much farther."

"Someday I'll see it," said Obadiah.

Father put his hand on Obadiah's shoulder. "I expect thee will," he said.

---

1. **breakwater** a wall that protects a harbor from the force of the waves.

155

THINKING IT OVER

Write your answers to these questions in your notebook or on a piece of paper. Remember to number your answers.

1. Why was the spyglass so special to Obadiah?
2. If Father had let Obadiah take the spyglass to Meeting, what do you think Obadiah would have done with it? If you had a spyglass, what would you use it for?
3. Why did being a pirate appeal so much to Obadiah? What name did he plan to take when he became a pirate?
4. Why do you think the Starbuck family was surprised when Obadiah said he wanted to be a pirate?
5. Obadiah's mother thought she had made a joke when she said, "Perhaps he could be a Friendly pirate." Can you explain this joke?
6. On page 140 Rachel asked Obadiah to

play house with her. He told her he was too big to play house. But on page 149 the story says that Obadiah played house for the rest of the afternoon. What made Obadiah change his mind?
7. How old do you think Obadiah was? What makes you think so?
8. What was Obadiah's father like? How did he help Obadiah solve his problem? Do you think he acted wisely?

TALKING IT OVER

You may want to share your ideas about these questions with others who have read *Obadiah the Bold*.

1. When you were Obadiah's age, what did you want to be when you grew up? If you have changed your mind since then, try and remember what it was that made you change your mind. Tell about it.
2. What would you like to be when you

grow up? Can you think of anything that would make you change your mind?

3. Does your family have any possession that has been handed down from generation to generation? Tell about it.

A LONG AGO STORY

The Starbuck family were not real people; the author just made them up. But the background of this story is real. Nantucket is a real place and long ago was a port for clipper ships. A Quaker family living at that time would have lived and dressed like the Starbuck family.

Which of these six statements show that this story took place long ago? Write these sentences in your notebook.

Big ships were driven by sails.
Obadiah got a spyglass for his birthday.
Ships often had wooden figures on their bows.

Obadiah's family got dressed up to go to Meeting.

Fearless pirates roamed the seven seas.

Obadiah played house with Rachel.

WHAT'S IN A NAME?

What is your first name? Do you know what it means? Names come from many languages. Obadiah is Hebrew and is the name of a book in the Bible. Philip means *lover of horses*. Barbara means *stranger,* Stephen means *crown,* and Alice means *truth.*

The question the poet writes about is one that every child is asked at some time. What do you think Obadiah would answer if you could have asked him this question at the end of the story?

THE QUESTION
by Karla Kuskin

People always say to me
"What do you think you'd like to be
When you grow up?"
And I say "Why,
I think I'd like to be the sky
Or be a plane or train or mouse
Or maybe be a haunted house
Or something furry, rough and wild . . .
Or maybe I will stay a child."

"The Question" from IN THE MIDDLE OF THE TREES by Karla Kuskin. Copyright © 1958 by Karla Kuskin. Reprinted with permission of Harper & Row, Publishers.

CAPTAIN JIM
by Rachel Field

There's not a man along the wharves
   So brown as Captain Jim,
Or half so spry, or blue of eye —
   I'm going to be like him
Some day — and have hip rubber boots,
   And pictures in tattoo
On arms and chest, and sit with the rest
   Of the men on the wharves, and chew.

Do you think Obadiah will grow up to be like Captain Jim?

"Captain Jim" from TAXIS AND TOADSTOOLS by Rachel Field. Copyright 1926 by Doubleday & Company, Inc. Reprinted by permission of Doubleday & Company, Inc. and The World's Work Ltd.

UNTIL I SAW THE SEA
by Lilian Moore

Until I saw the sea
I did not know
that wind
could wrinkle water so.

I never knew
that sun
could splinter a whole sea of blue.

Nor
did I know before,
a sea breathes in and out
upon a shore.

Who do you think is taking the trip that this poem tells about? Will they get to Bombay?

ALL ABOARD FOR BOMBAY
by Leroy F. Jackson

All aboard for Bombay,
   All aboard for Rome!
Leave your little sisters
   And your loving aunts at home.

Bring a bit of bailing wire,
   A pocketful of nails,
And half a dozen wienewursts
   For every man that sails.

Tell Terry Tagg, when you go by,
   Be sure to bring his dog.
All aboard for Bombay
   On a floating cedar log!

"All Aboard for Bombay" from PETER PATTER BOOK by Leroy F. Jackson. Copyright 1918, 1946 Rand McNally & Company. Reprinted by permission of Robert C. Jackson.

COLLECTORS' ITEMS

HIDE AND SEEK FOG
by Alvin Tresselt

A terrible fog came to a village on Cape Cod. The grown-ups were unhappy, but the children loved it. They played hide-and-seek, toasted marshmallows, and got lost in front of their own houses.

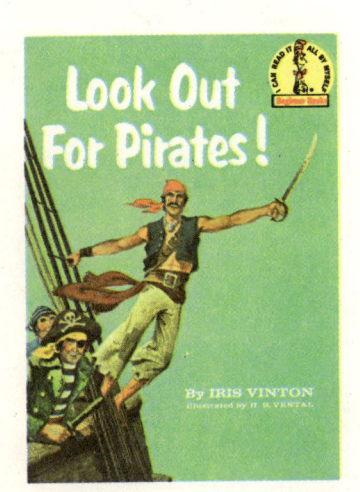

LOOK OUT FOR PIRATES!
by Iris Vinton

Captain Jim and his crew match wits with pirates who are after their chest of gold.

PIRATES & PRIVATEERS
by Edith McCall

Here is the story of an exciting era in our nation's past, a time when Captain Kidd and Bluebeard the Pirate sailed the American coastal waters.

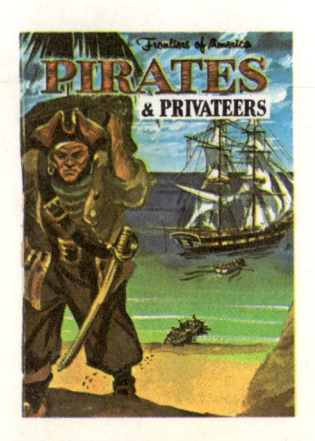

ADVENTURE AT MONT-SAINT-MICHEL
by Napoli

A French girl lived by the sea. When the tide rose, the sea came almost to her door. When the tide went out, the sea disappeared over the horizon. Where did it go? One day the girl set off to find out.

HEAR YE OF BOSTON
by Polly Curren

The city of Boston was a battleground for the beginning of freedom in America. The text in this book is easy and interesting, and the large colorful pictures give a splendid portrait of this historical city.

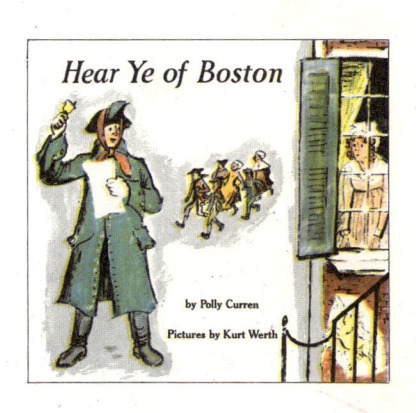

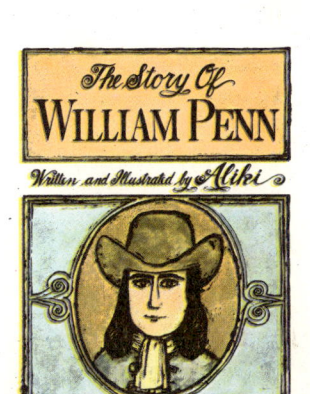

THE STORY OF WILLIAM PENN
by Aliki

This is a biography of William Penn, the Quaker leader who founded the colony of Pennsylvania in 1682.

ALIKI BRANDENBERG is a well-known author and illustrator of children's books. She graduated from the Museum College of Art in Philadelphia. From 1956 to 1960, she lived in Switzerland. It was there that she completed her first children's book, *The Story of William Tell*.

Since September 1960, Aliki has been living in New York City with her husband, Franz, and their children, Jason and Alexa.

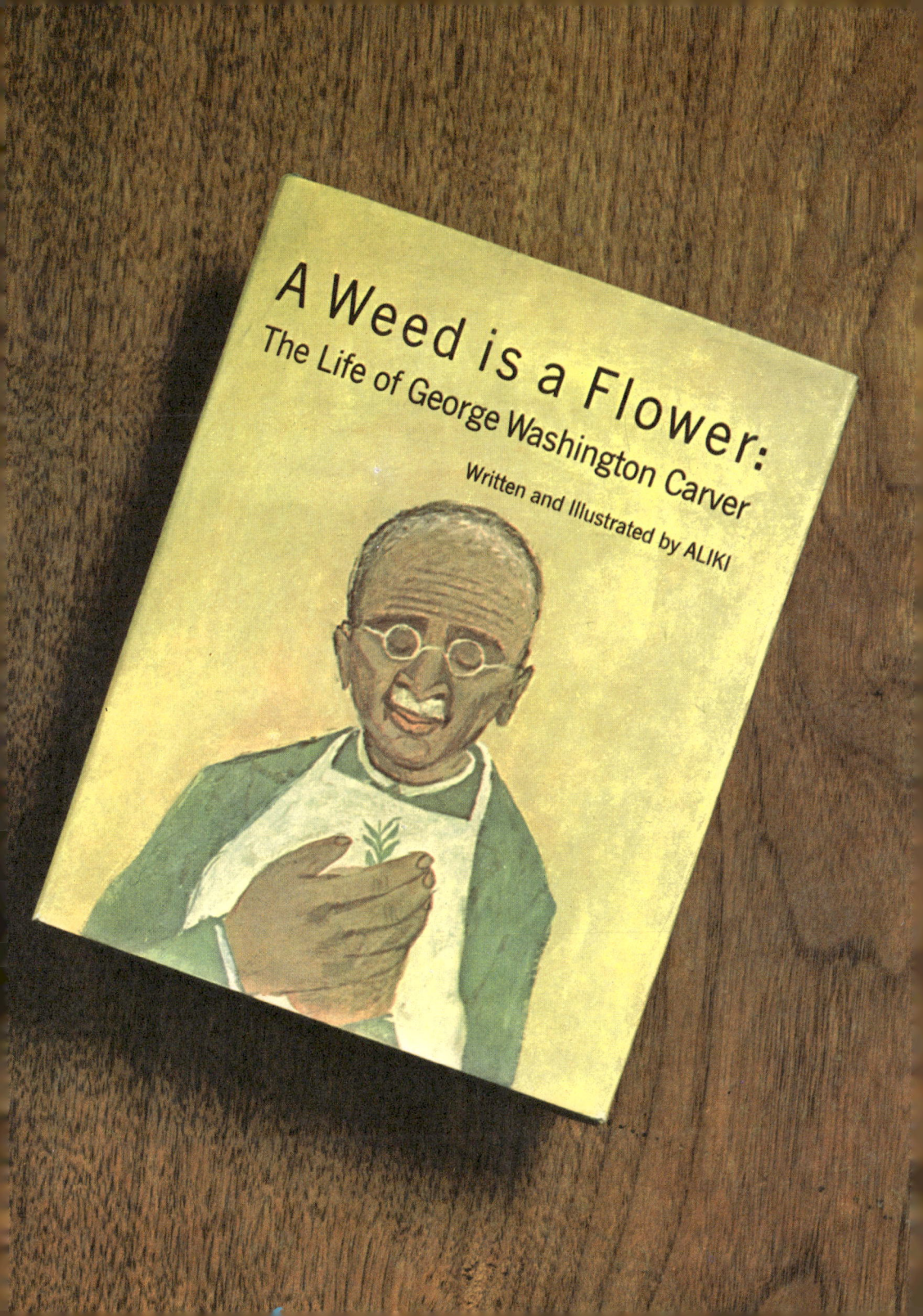

A Weed is a Flower:
The Life of George Washington Carver

Written and Illustrated by ALIKI

A weed is a flower growing in the wrong place. That is what George Washington Carver, the famous Negro scientist, used to say. When you read this book, you will learn what he meant.

A Weed is a Flower:

The Life of George Washington Carver

written and illustrated by *Aliki*

Prentice-Hall, Inc., Englewood Cliffs, N.J.

From the book A WEED IS A FLOWER by Aliki
© 1965 by Aliki Brandenberg
Published by Prentice-Hall, Inc., Englewood Cliffs, New Jersey

for Lisa, Jim, and Stephen

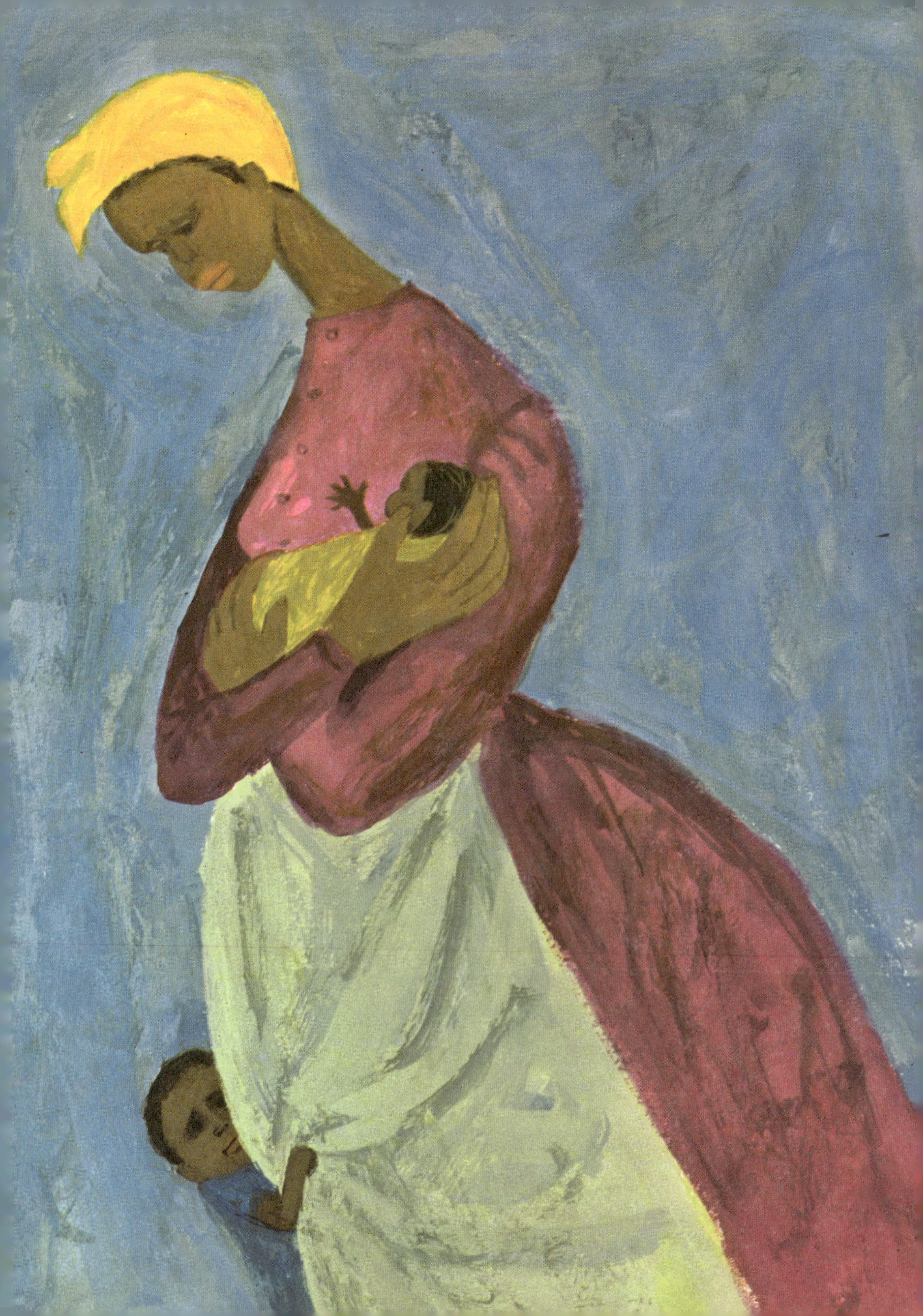

When George Washington Carver was born, he had many things against him. He was a sick, weak, little baby. His father had just died, and his mother was left alone to care for him and for his brother, James. And even worse, he was the son of slaves. There was no hope for the future.

But George Washington Carver was no ordinary man. He was a man who turned evil into good, despair into hope, and hatred into love. He was a man who devoted his whole life to helping his people and the world around him.

This is his story.

George Washington Carver was born in Missouri in 1860—more than a hundred years ago. It was a terrible time. Mean men rode silently in the night, kidnapping slaves from their owners and harming those who tried to stop them.

One night, a band of these men rode up to the farm of Moses Carver, who owned George and his mother, Mary. Everyone ran in fear. But before Mary could hide her baby, the men came and snatched them both and rode away into the night.

Moses Carver sent a man to look for them. Mary was never found. But in a few days, the man returned with a small bundle wrapped in his coat and tied to the back of his saddle. It was the baby, George.

Moses and his wife, Susan, cared for Mary's children. George remained small and weak. But as he grew, they saw he was an unusual child. He wanted to know about everything around him. He asked about the rain, the flowers, and the insects. He asked questions the Carvers couldn't answer.

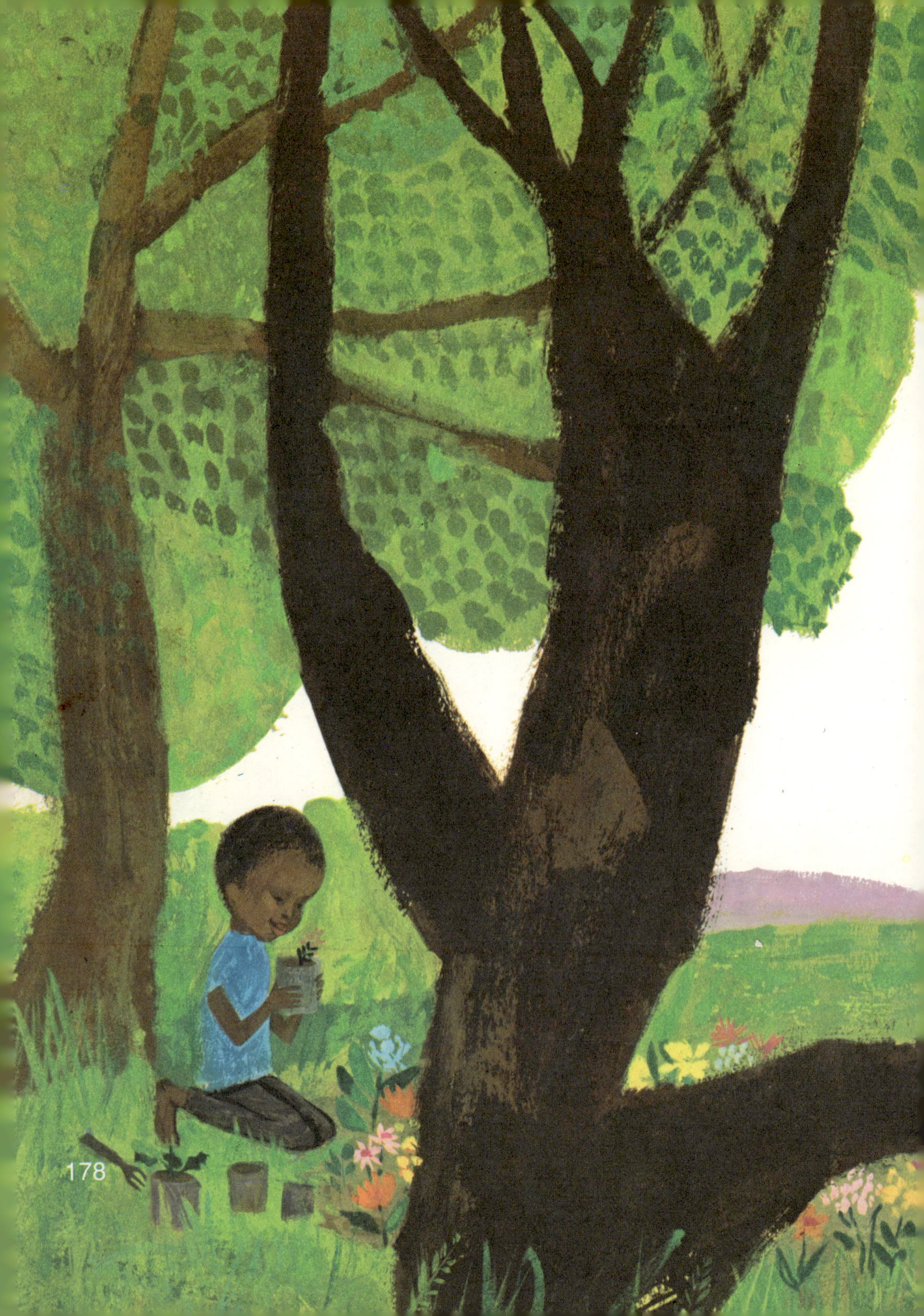

When he was very young, George kept a garden where he spent hours each day caring for his plants. If they weren't growing well, he found out why. Soon they were healthy and blooming. In winter he covered his plants to protect them. In spring he planted new seeds. George looked after each plant as though it was the only one in his garden.

Neighbors began to ask George's advice about their plants, and soon he was known as the Plant Doctor.

As time went on, George wondered about more and more things. He wanted to learn and yearned to go to school.

In the meantime, the slaves had been freed, but schools nearby were not open to Negroes. So when he was ten, George left his brother, his garden, and the Carver farm and went off to find the answers to his questions.

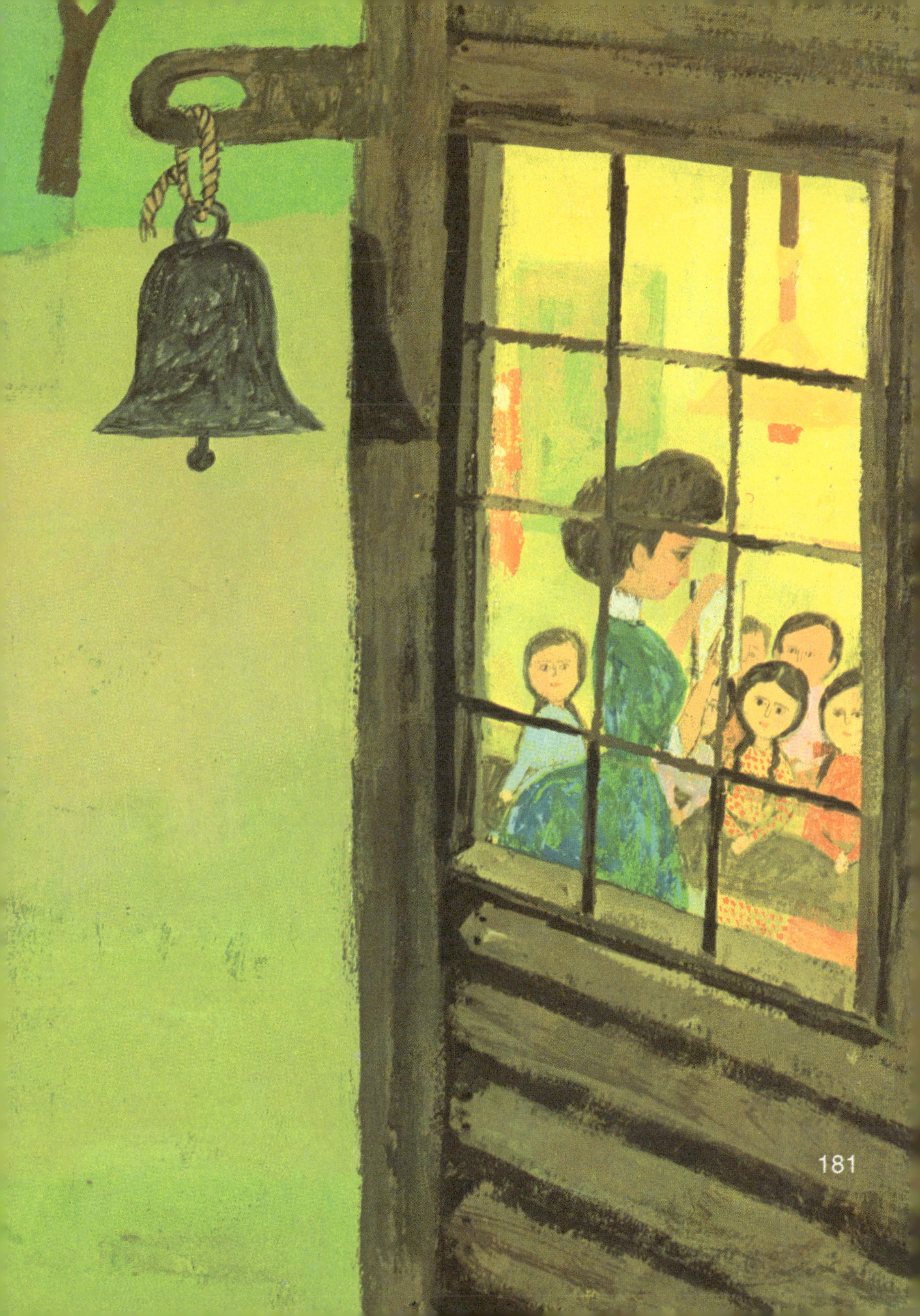

Wherever George Washington Carver found schools, he stayed. He worked for people to earn his keep. He scrubbed their floors, washed their clothes, and baked their bread. Whatever George did, he did well. Even the smallest chore was important to him.

Some people took George in as their son. First he stayed with Mariah and Andy Watkins, who were like parents to him. Then he moved to Kansas and lived with "Aunt" Lucy and "Uncle" Seymour. They, too, loved this quiet boy who was so willing to help.

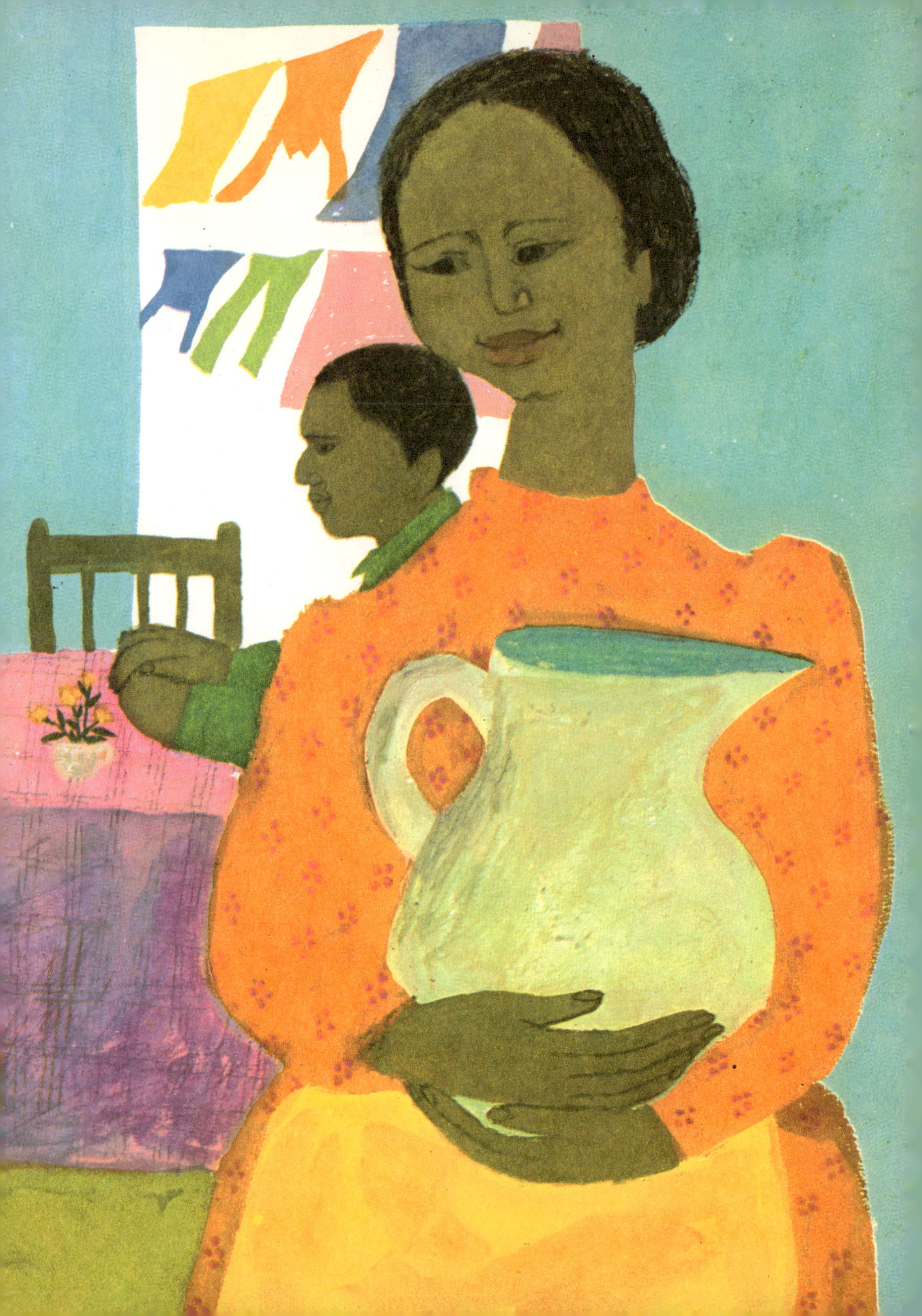

George worked hard for many years, always trying to save enough money for college. Other boys, who had parents to help them, were able to enter college much sooner than George. He was thirty before he had saved enough. Still, it was not that simple. All colleges would not admit Negroes, even if they had the money to pay.

George was not discouraged. He moved to Iowa and found a college which was glad to have a Negro student.

At college George continued to work. He opened a laundry where he washed his schoolmates' clothes.

And he continued to learn. His teachers and friends soon realized that this earnest young man was bursting with talents. He played the piano, he sang beautifully, and he was an outstanding painter. In fact, for a time he thought of becoming an artist.

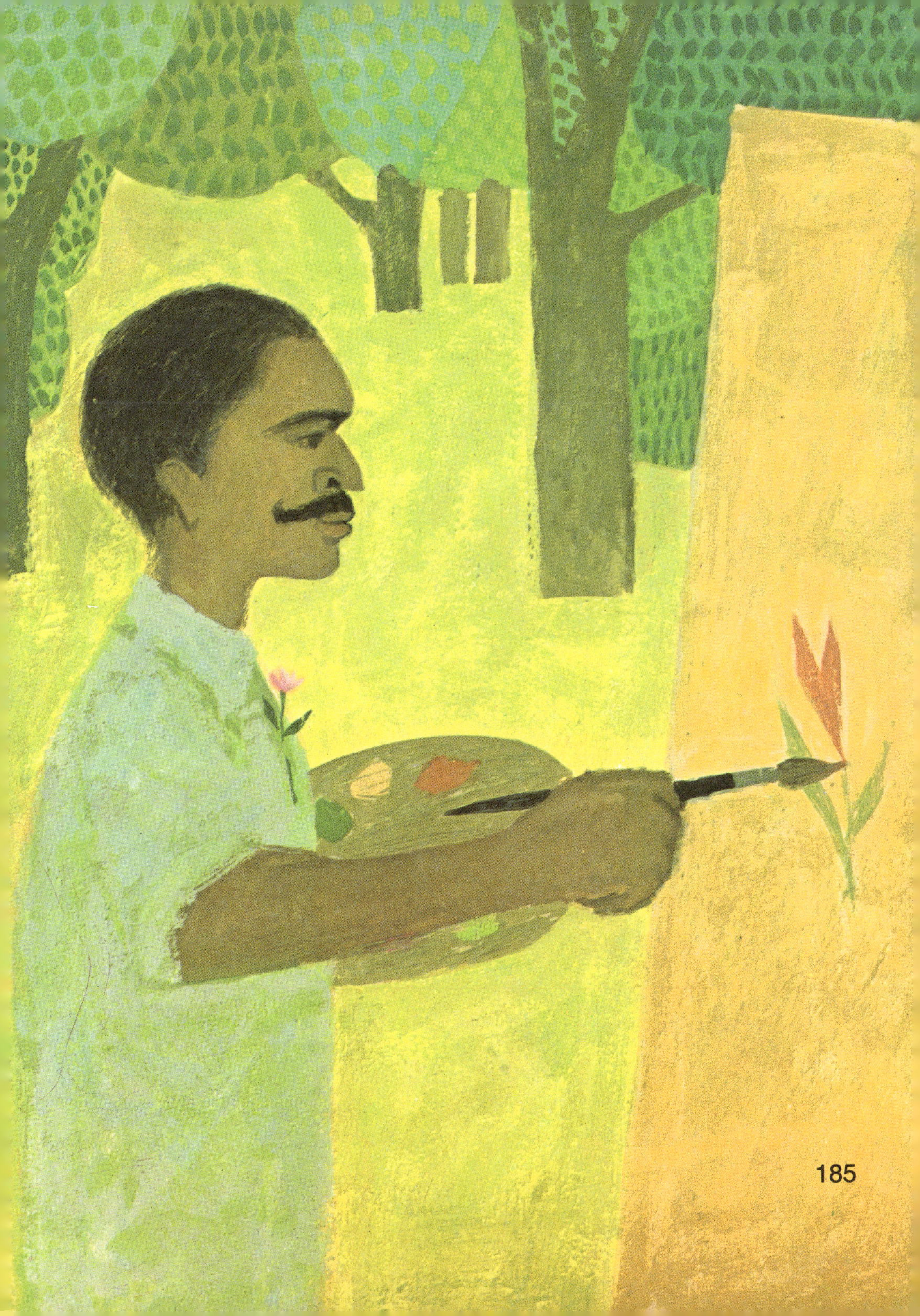

186

But the more George thought of what he wanted to do, the more he wanted to help his people, and he remembered that his neighbors used to call him the Plant Doctor.

He had never forgotten his love for plants. In all the years he had wandered, he always had something growing in his room.

So George Washington Carver chose to study agriculture. He learned about plants, flowers, and soil. He learned the names of the weeds. Even they were important to him. He often said: a weed is a flower growing in the wrong place.

He still asked questions. If no person or book could answer them, he found the answers himself. He experimented with plants and found secrets no one else knew.

When George finished college, he began to teach. He was asked to go to Alabama, where a college for Negroes needed his talent. It was there, at Tuskegee Institute, that George Washington Carver made his life.

In Alabama, Professor Carver taught his students and the poor Negro farmers, who earned their livelihood from the soil. He taught them how to make their crops grow better.

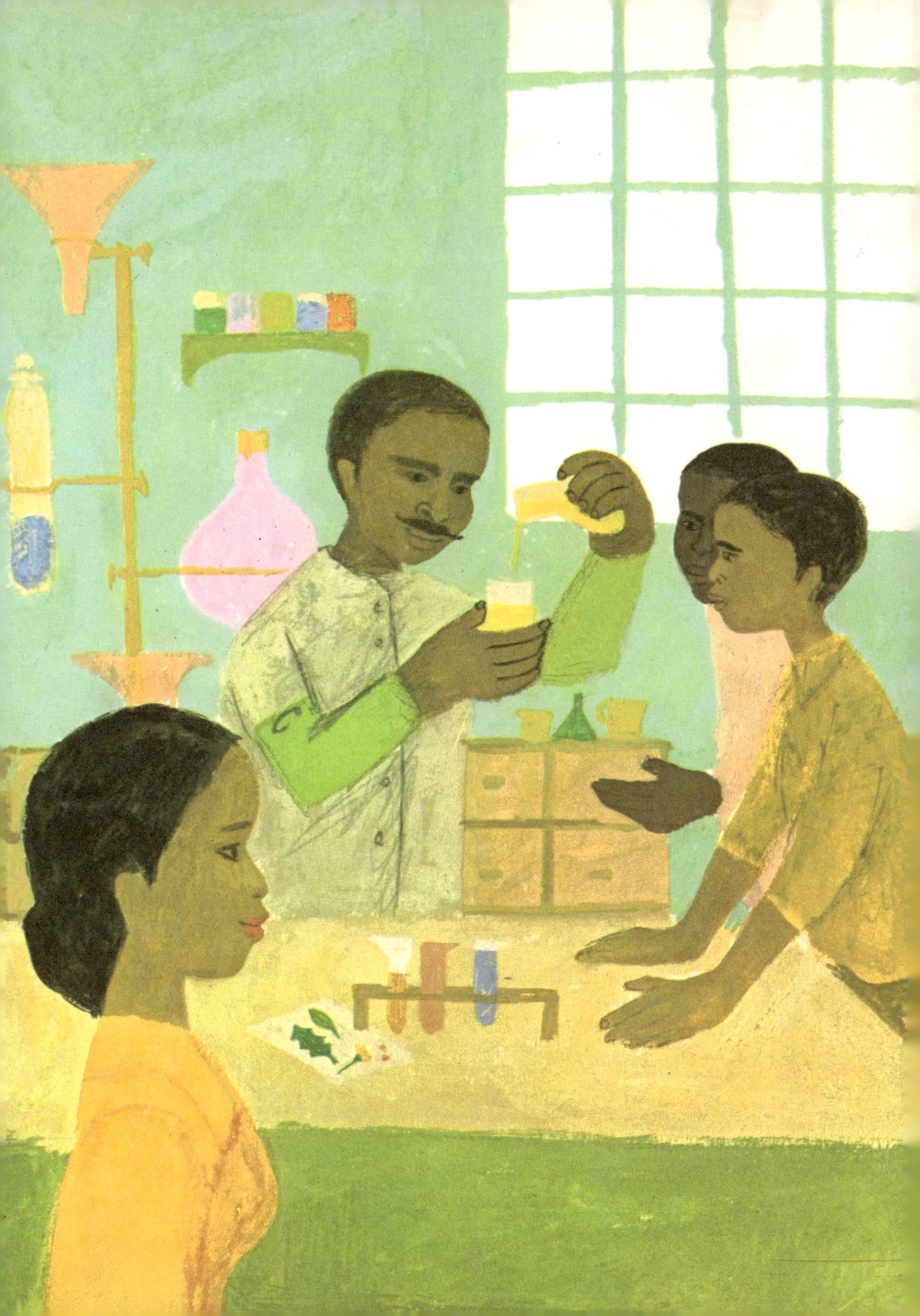

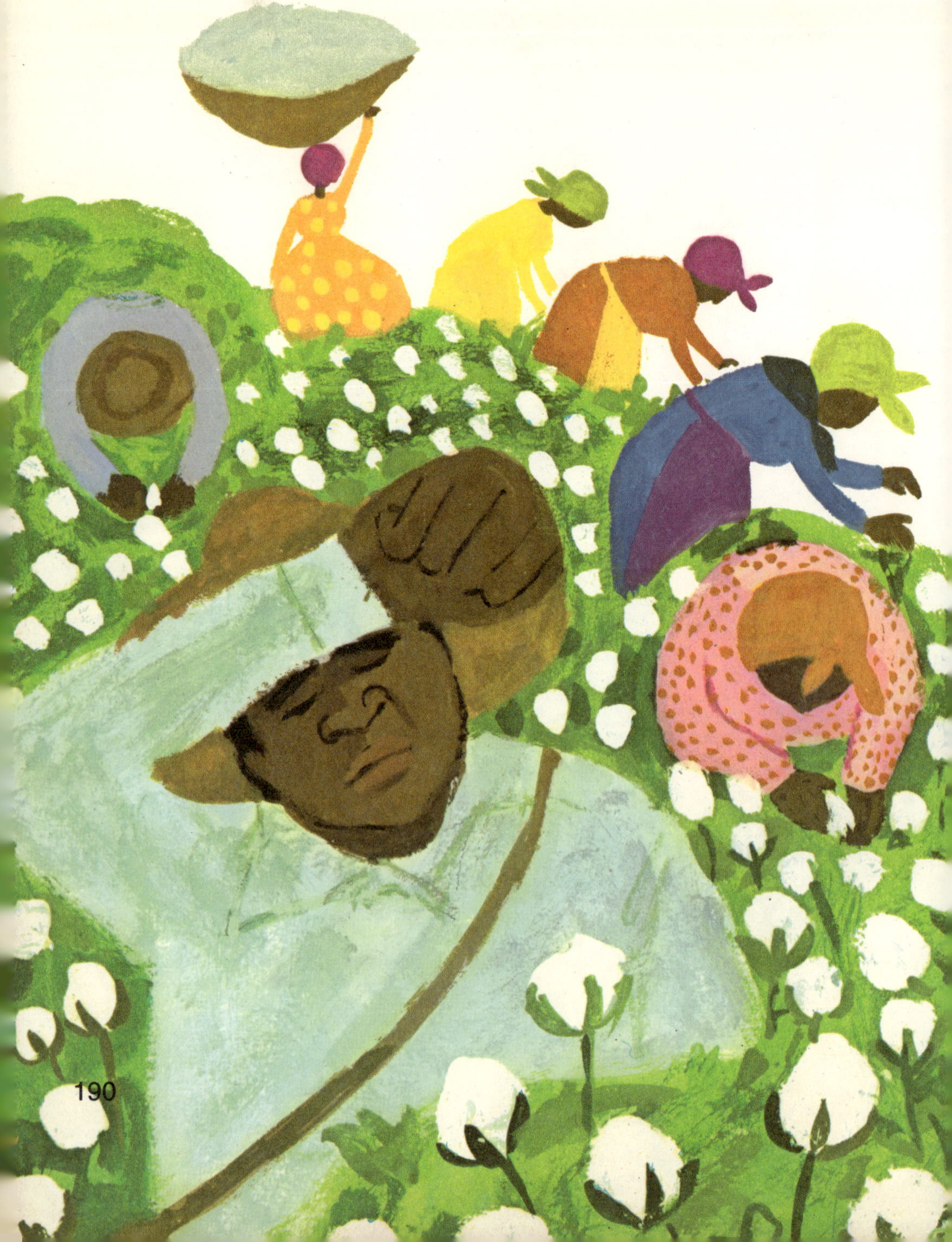

Most of the farmers raised cotton. But sometimes the crops were destroyed by rain or insects, and the farmers couldn't earn enough to eat.

Professor Carver told them to plant other things as well. Sweet potatoes and peanuts were good crops. They were easy to grow. He said that raising only cotton harmed the soil. It was better if different crops were planted each year.

The farmers did not want to listen. They were afraid to plant peanuts and sweet potatoes. They were sure that no one would buy them.

But Professor Carver had experimented in his laboratory. He had found that many things could be made from the sweet potato. He made soap, coffee, and starch. He made more than a hundred things from the sweet potato.

And even though people in those days called peanuts "monkey food," Professor Carver said they were good for people, too. Besides, he found that still more things could be made from the peanut. Paper, ink, shaving cream, sauces, linoleum, shampoo, and even milk! In fact, he made three hundred different products from the peanut.

Once, when important guests were expected at Tuskegee, Dr. Carver chose the menu. The guests sat around the table and enjoyed a meal of soup, creamed mock chicken, bread, salad, coffee, candy, cake, and ice cream. Imagine their surprise when they learned that the meal was made entirely from peanuts!

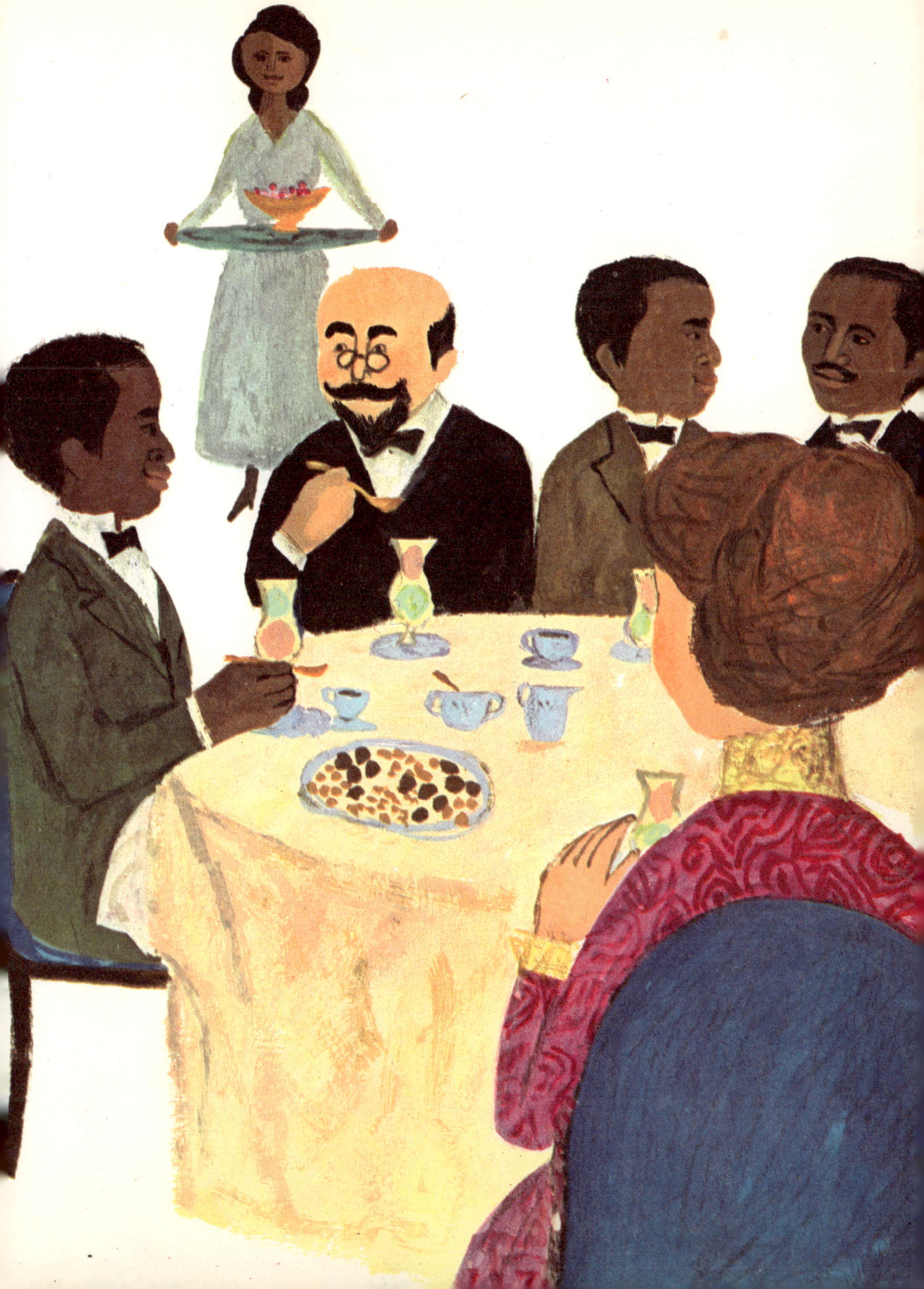

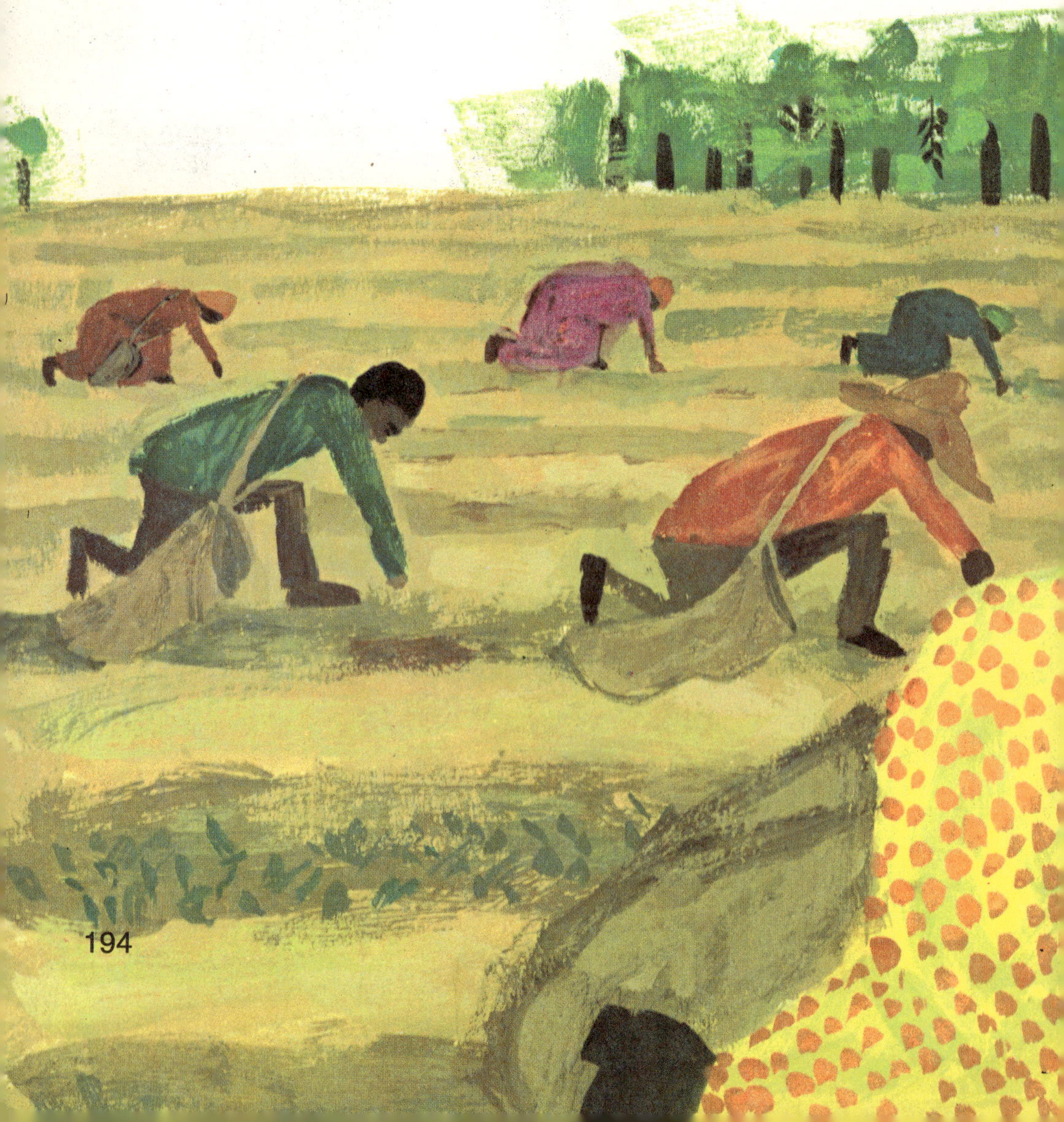

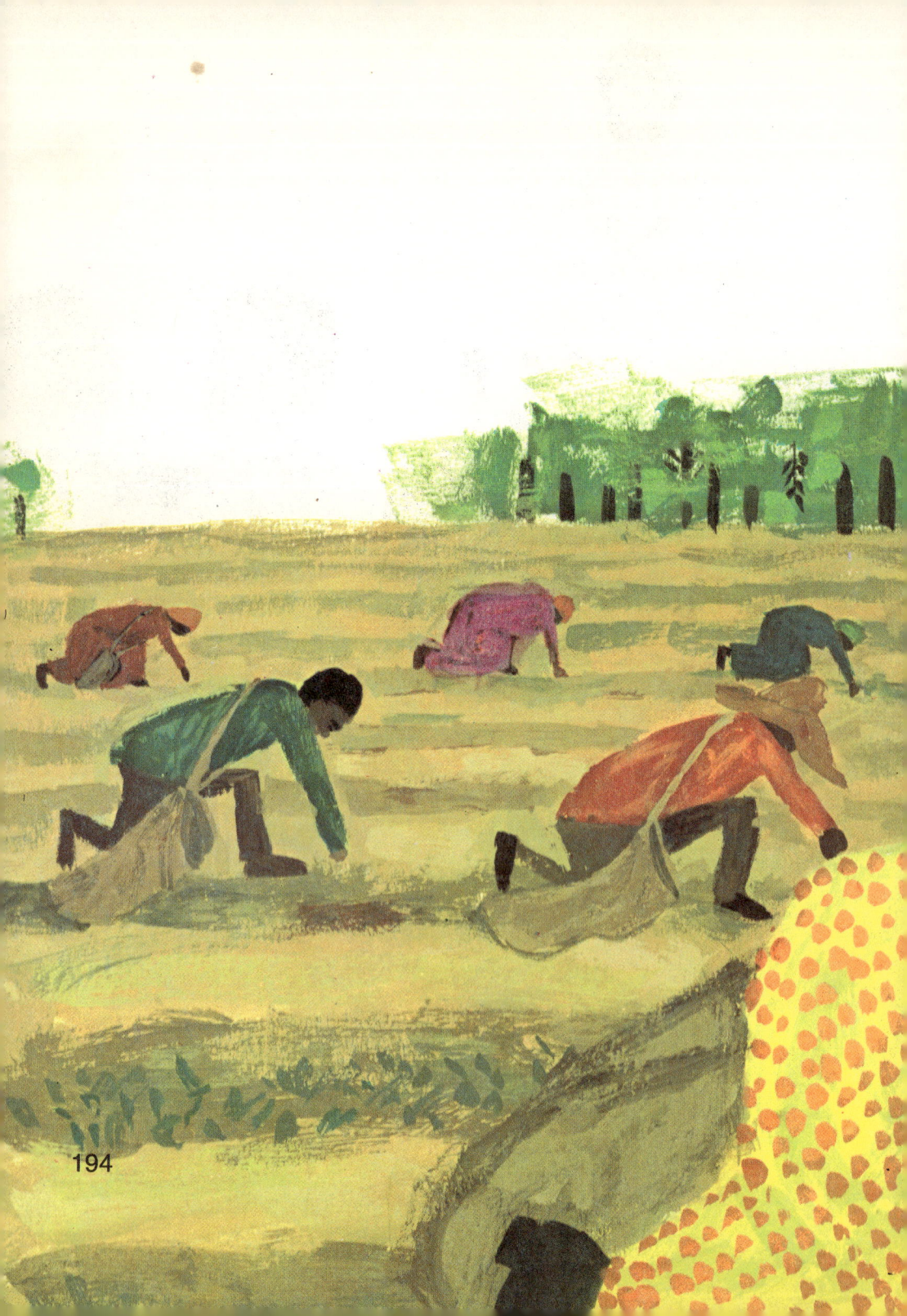

Slowly, the farmers listened to George Washington Carver. They planted peanuts and sweet potatoes, and before they knew it these became two of the most important crops in Alabama.

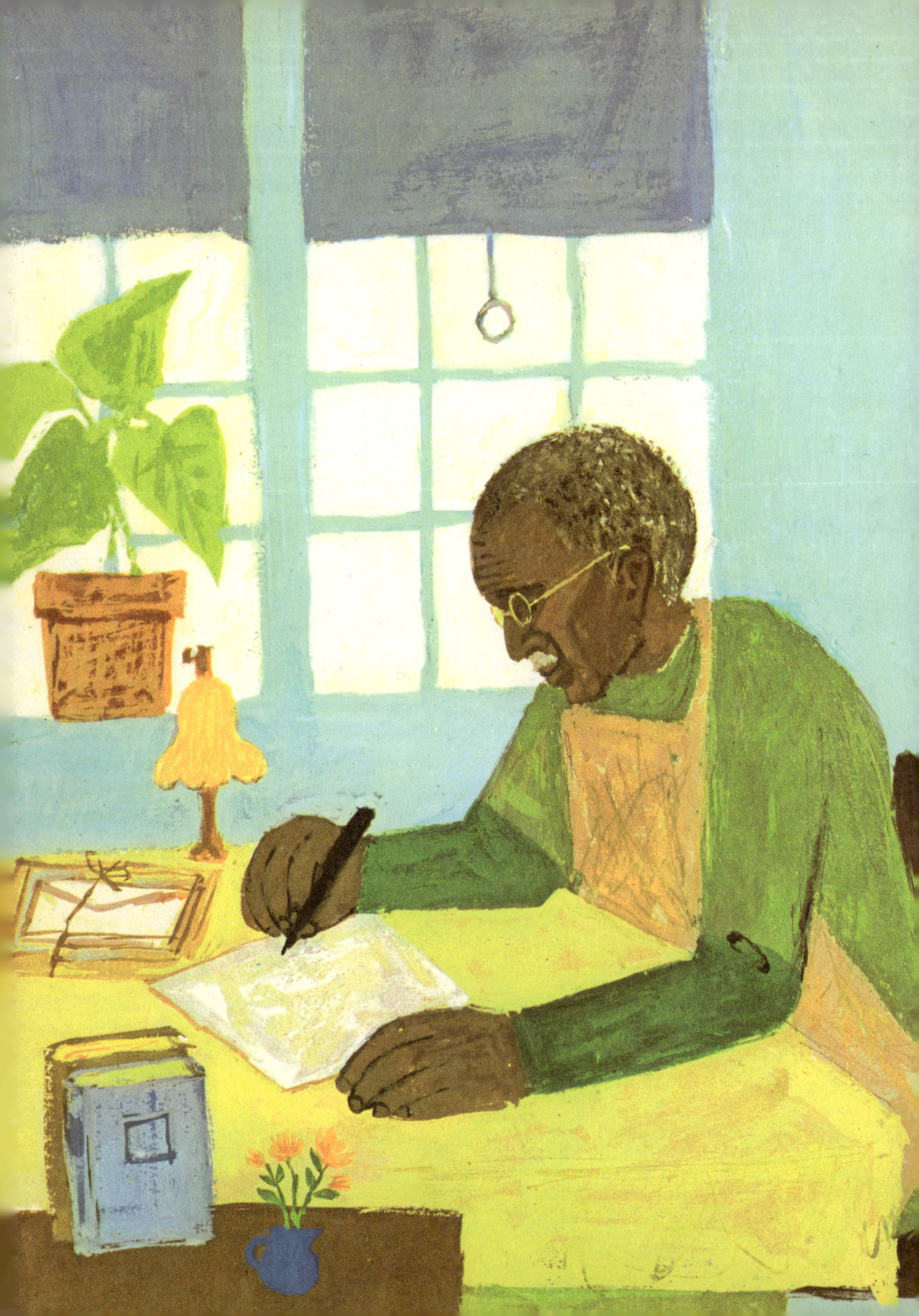

Soon the whole country knew about Dr. Carver and the great things he was doing. He was honored by Presidents and other important people. Every day his mailbox bulged with letters from farmers and scientists who wanted his advice. He was offered great sums of money which he turned down. Money was not important to him. He did not even bother to cash many of the checks he received.

Throughout his life, George Washington Carver asked nothing of others. He sought only to help. He lived alone and tended to his own needs. He washed his clothes and patched them, too. He used the soap he made and ate the food he grew.

Dr. Carver was asked to speak in many parts of the world, but he did not leave Tuskegee often. He had things to do. He continued to paint. He worked in his greenhouse and in his laboratory, where he discovered many things. He discovered that dyes could be made from plants and colors from the Alabama clay. Even when he was over eighty and close to death, Dr. Carver kept working. Night after night, while the rest of the town lay asleep, a light still shone in his window.

The baby born with no hope for the future grew into one of the great scientists of his country. George Washington Carver, with his goodness and devotion, helped not only his own people, but all peoples of the world.

THINKING IT OVER

Write your answers to these questions in your notebook or on a piece of paper. Remember to number your answers.

1. George Washington Carver often said that a weed is a flower growing in the wrong place. What do you think he meant? Do you think Aliki chose a good title for her book about Carver? Why or why not?
2. What did it mean to be born the son of slaves? How did George get his last name?
3. How would you describe the kind of child George was? Do you think he would have been fun to have for a friend? Why or why not?
4. How did George learn so much about plants, flowers, and soil? Why was he called the Plant Doctor?
5. What is the study of agriculture? What made George choose to study agriculture?

6. On page 173 the author says that George Washington Carver was a "man who devoted his whole life to helping his people and the world around him." Who were his people? How did he help them and the world around him?
7. How did conditions for the Negro change during Carver's lifetime?
8. You have read two stories about people who lived long ago—*Obadiah the Bold* and *A Weed is a Flower*. Which story is about someone who actually lived? Which story is about someone the author made up?
9. Name other famous people who have helped the world around them.

TALKING IT OVER

Perhaps you would like to share your ideas about the following questions with others who have read *A Weed is a Flower*.

1. What do you think was George Washington Carver's greatest gift to man?
2. What other famous people can you think of who were born in poor homes and with little hope for the future?
3. Do you think George Washington Carver's life would have been easier and better if he had grown up today instead of one hundred years ago? Why or why not?
4. What might have happened to George if he had never been returned to the Carvers?
5. George Washington Carver was a scientist. Think about the way that he studied plants. How would you describe a scientist?

ON YOUR OWN

1. Booker T. Washington was the head of the college in Alabama where Carver spent most of his life. What can you find out about this great Negro?

2. The peanut is not really a nut but is more closely related to the pea and the bean. What were some of the three hundred uses Carver found for the peanut? What recipes can you find that use peanuts? Perhaps you would like to try one of those given in your notebook.
3. Take a piece of blank paper. Draw lines which divide your paper into three parts. Now draw three pictures, one in each section of your paper, that you think show the beginning, the middle, and the end of Carver's life.
4. Choose one of the famous people from the list you made to answer question 9 on page 202. Find out as much as you can about him and prepare a report in which you tell why you chose him and what his contributions were.
5. Perhaps you are ready to write an autobiography. *Auto* means *self,* so an autobiography means a biography

of yourself. Or you could choose a person whom you know and gather enough facts to write his or her biography.

ABOUT THE PICTURES

1. The author and illustrator of this book are the same person. Do you think this makes the book better? Why or why not?
2. Notice how the artist has repeated the drawing of a flower in many of the pictures. Why do you think she did this?
3. What do you learn about Carver's feelings from studying the pictures on pages 178, 180, 182, 186, and 196?
4. Suppose there were no text in this book. Do you think someone could learn about Carver's life by just looking at the pictures?

If George Washington Carver had been a poet, do you think he might have written a poem like this?

WEEDS
by Charlotte Zolotow

I can't understand
people who hate weeds.
Dandelions and buttercups
and clover for the bees
and maybe some Queen Anne's lace
are all a garden needs.

THE SEED
by Aileen Fisher

How does it know,
this little seed,
if it is to grow
to a flower or weed,
if it is to be
a vine or shoot,
or grow to a tree
with a long deep root?
A seed is so small
Where do you suppose
it stores up all
of the things it knows?

"The Seed" from UP THE WINDY HILL by Aileen Fisher. Published by Scott, Foresman and Company.

A spark in the sun,
this tiny flower has roots
   deep in the cool earth.
      by Harry Behn

Out of one wintry
twig, one bud, one blossom's-worth
   at long last of warmth!
      by Ransetsu

Spring is almost gone,
so now this silly old tree
   decides to bloom!
      by Buson

What do you notice about these three poems? After you decide, try to write one of your own.

From CRICKET SONGS: JAPANESE HAIKU, translated and © 1964, by Harry Behn. Reprinted by permission of Harcourt, Brace & World, Inc. and Curtis Brown Ltd.

How do you think George Washington Carver would think of a dandelion — as a weed or as a flower? This poet thinks of it in an entirely different way.

DANDELION
by Hilda Conkling, age 9

O little soldier with the golden helmet,
What are you guarding on my lawn?
You with your green gun
And your yellow beard,
Why do you stand so stiff?
There is only the grass to fight!

"Dandelion" from POEMS BY A LITTLE GIRL by Hilda Conkling. Copyright 1920 by J. B. Lippincott Company; copyright renewed 1948 by Hilda Conkling. Published by J. B. Lippincott Company.

COLLECTORS' ITEMS

BOOKER T. WASHINGTON: LEADER OF HIS PEOPLE
by Lillie G. Patterson

Like George Washington Carver, Booker T. Washington had to struggle for an education. This book tells you about it.

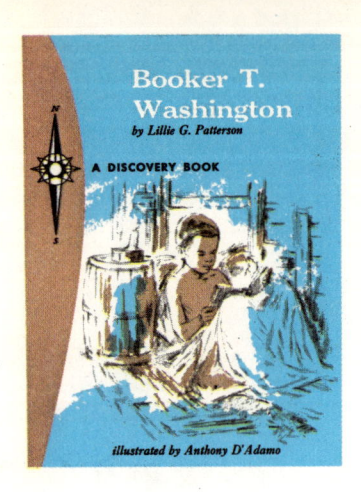

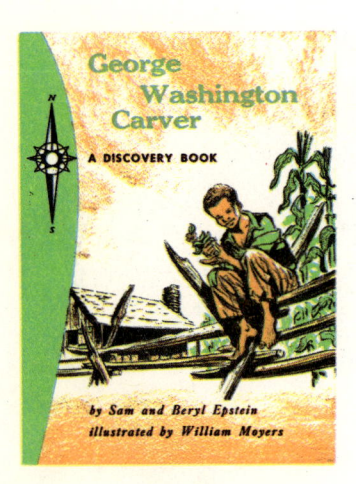

GEORGE WASHINGTON CARVER: NEGRO SCIENTIST
by Samuel and Beryl Epstein

It was exciting to be a student in Carver's class at Tuskegee. This book will tell you about his work as a professor as well as many other interesting things about this great man.

THE STORY OF JOHNNY APPLESEED
by Aliki

Johnny Appleseed was a gentle pioneer who spent his life roaming the United States and planting apple trees wherever he went. His is a true story from the American past; trees that he planted can still be seen today.

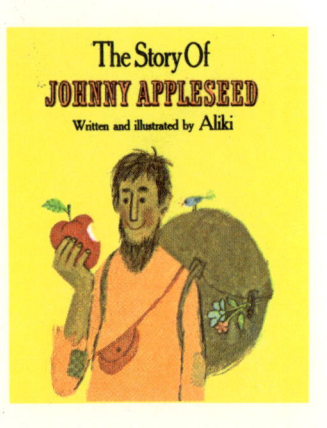

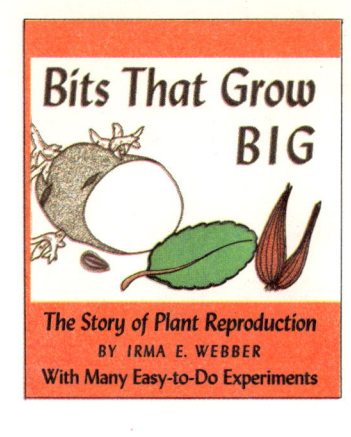

BITS THAT GROW BIG
by Irma E. Webber

A book that contains all the information needed to conduct many experiments about plants.

LIONS IN THE GRASS
by Phyllis S. Busch

This is the story of the dandelion. It tells how it got its name, how it develops from a seed, how it manufactures its own food, and many other facts about this sometime weed, sometime flower.

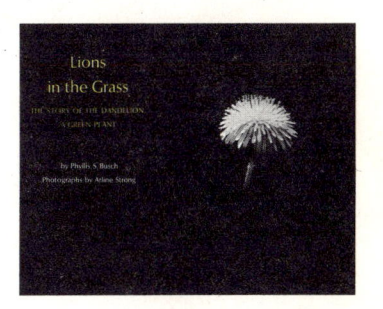

PICK A RAINCOAT, PICK A WHISTLE
by Lillian Bason 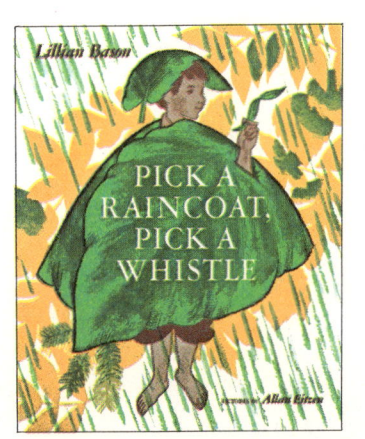

Leaves have many different uses around the world. Some people believe they help cure toothaches. In hot countries leaves are often used to build houses. Sometimes they even serve as plates or raincoats.

EUGENE FERN believes that living happily ever after isn't just for storybooks. He thinks everyone can be happy if we all learn that the important things in life are people—not money or possessions.

Mr. Fern was born in Detroit and grew up in Brooklyn. He studied at art schools and worked at many different jobs: on farms, in an art gallery, as a cement mixer, and as a machinist. Later he graduated from Columbia University. He is now a college teacher and lives on Long Island with his wife and children.

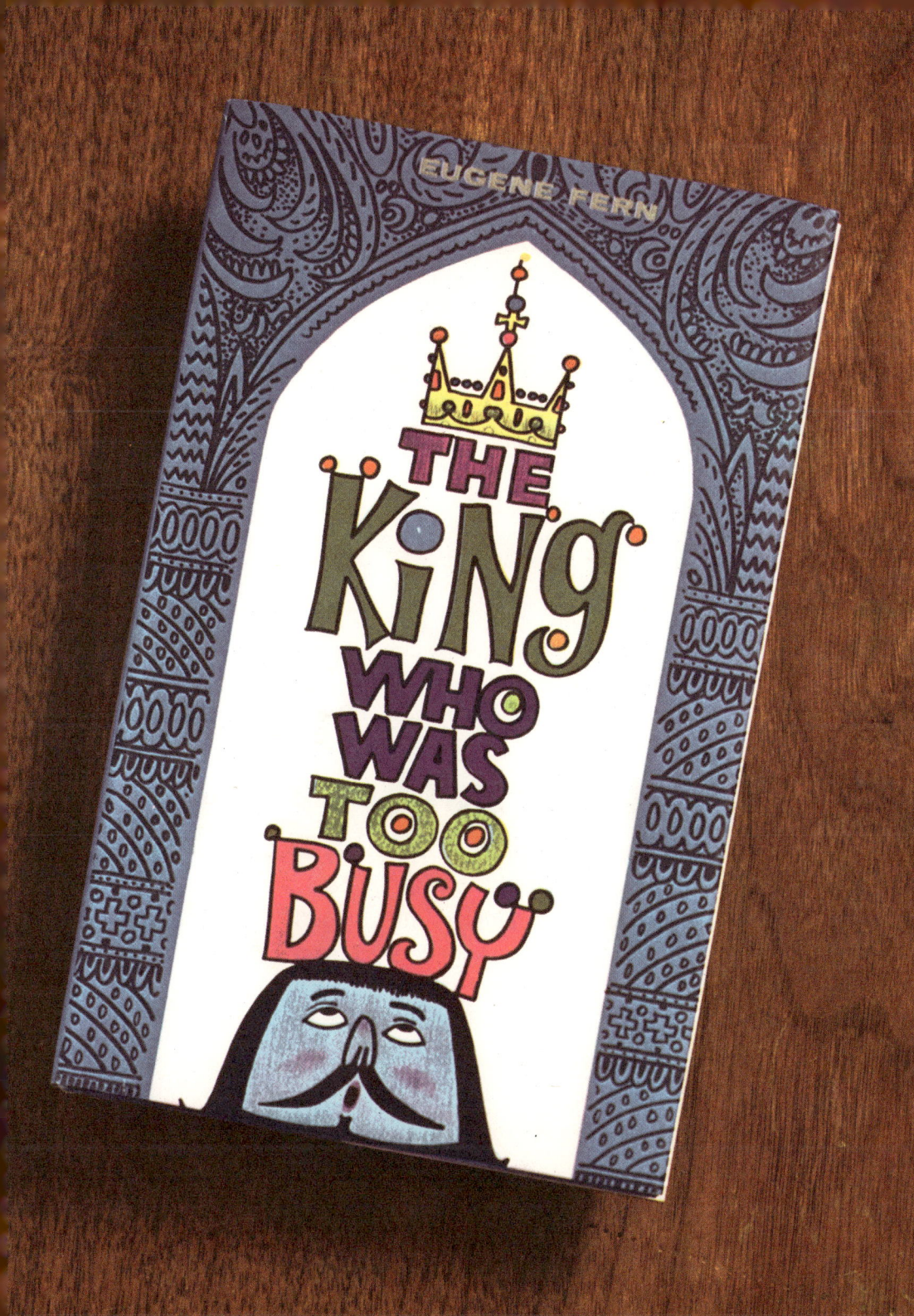

EUGENE FERN

THE KING WHO WAS TOO BUSY

Money and power are not the most important things in life. It's what we *are* that really counts. The king in this story had forgotten this. Then something happened to remind him — just in time.

EUGENE FERN

THE KING WHO WAS TOO BUSY

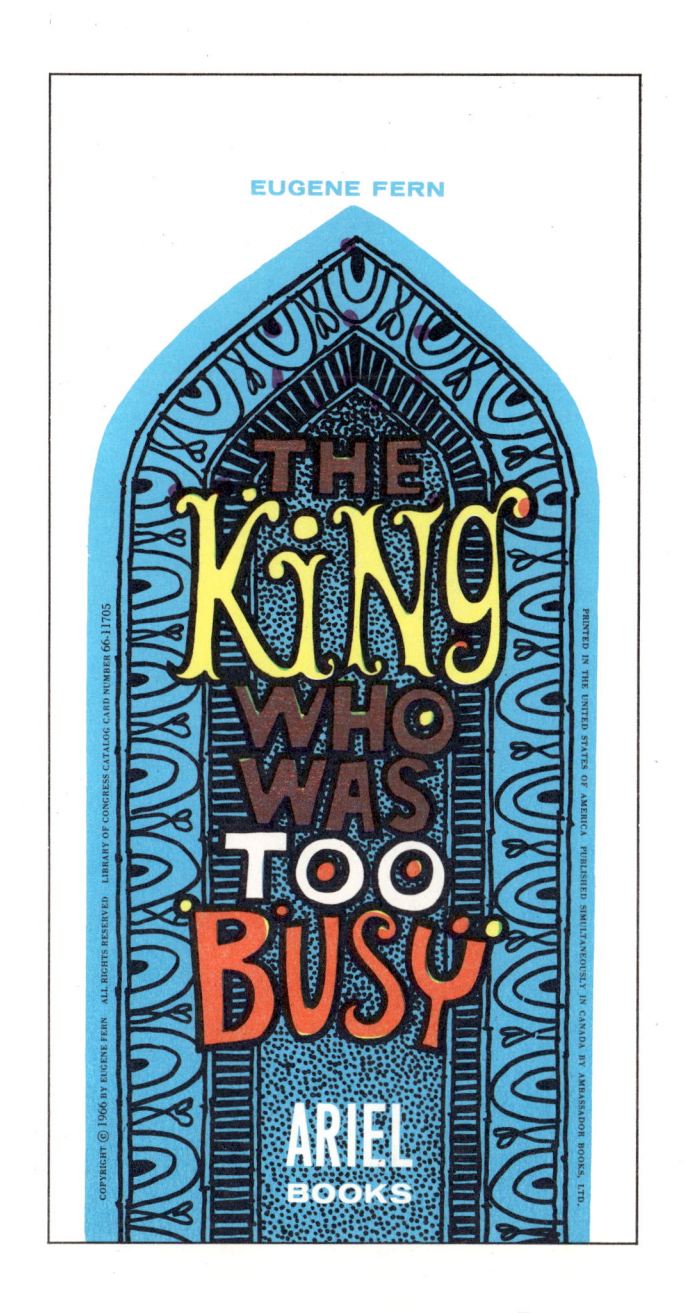

ARIEL BOOKS

Reprinted with permission of Farrar, Straus & Giroux, Inc.
And The World's Work Ltd.
THE KING WHO WAS TOO BUSY by Eugene Fern
Copyright © 1966 by Eugene Fern

Once there was a little king who ruled a small kingdom far away in a small land.

He was a good king. His people trusted him, for he was always ready to help anyone in trouble. His friends were fond of him, for he always found time to share a joke or a game of cards with them. His little daughter adored him, for he was never too busy to tell her stories . . .

... or walk with her through the countryside.

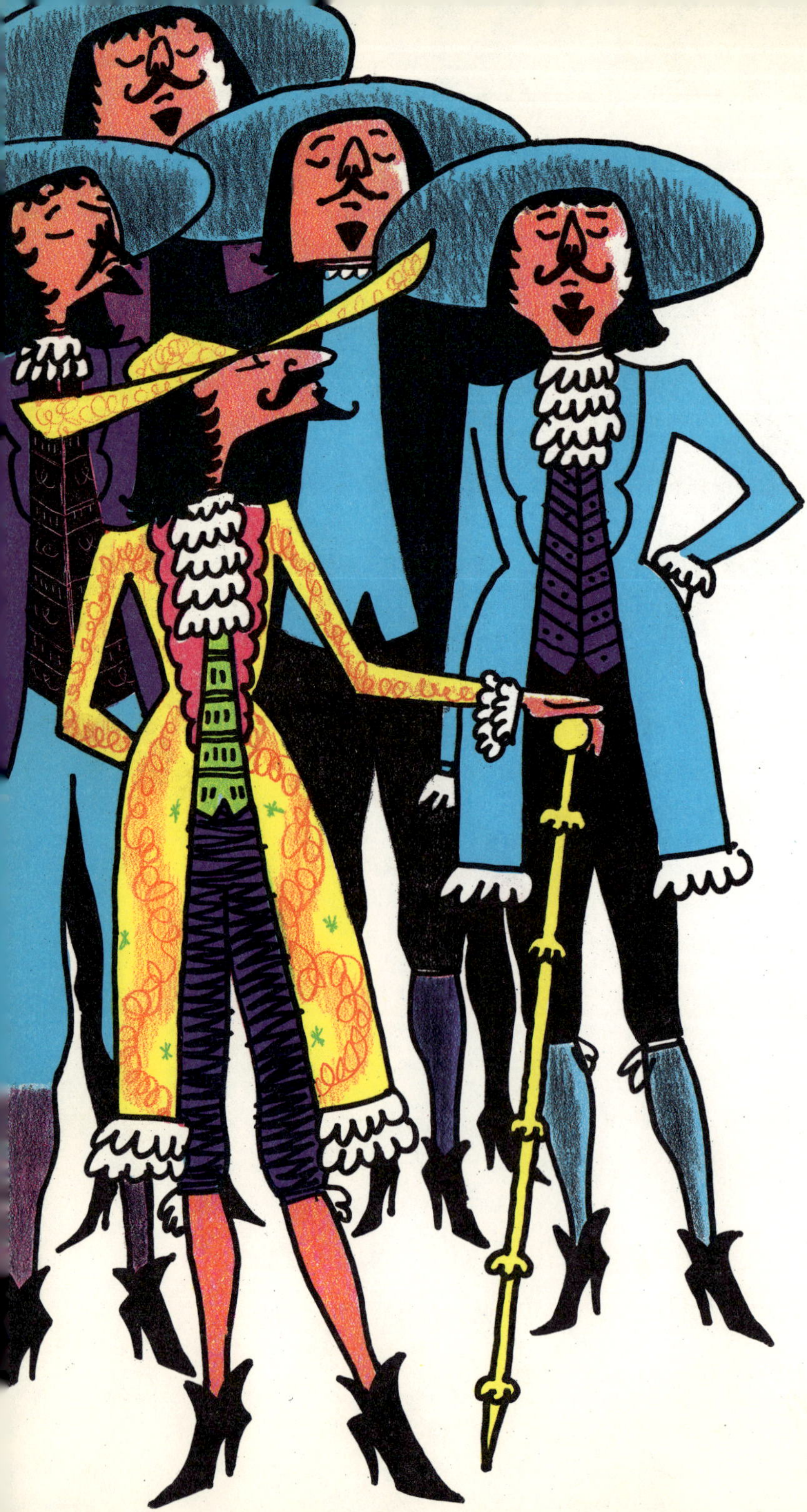

However, one day a visitor from a great kingdom across the sea came to speak of a royal alliance. He took one look at the small kingdom and said:

"Why, you foolish little thing,
Dare you call yourself a king?
You have no pictures on your walls.
You have no statues in your halls.
You own no extra-fancy chairs.
You have no rugs upon your stairs.
You have no army, own no boats.
You have no diamonds on your coats.
You have no storerooms filled with gold.
Your robe is shabby, torn, and old.
You have no ministers at all,
And your crown is very small.
Remember this important thing:
It's the crown that makes the king.

"I can see that I'm wasting my time here," he added, and sailed away without bothering even to say good-by.

From that day on, the king was a changed man. He had never thought much about what a king was supposed to be like. Now that he knew, he was terribly ashamed. He felt small and very unimportant. Then and there he decided to become a great king and to have all the precious things a great king should have.

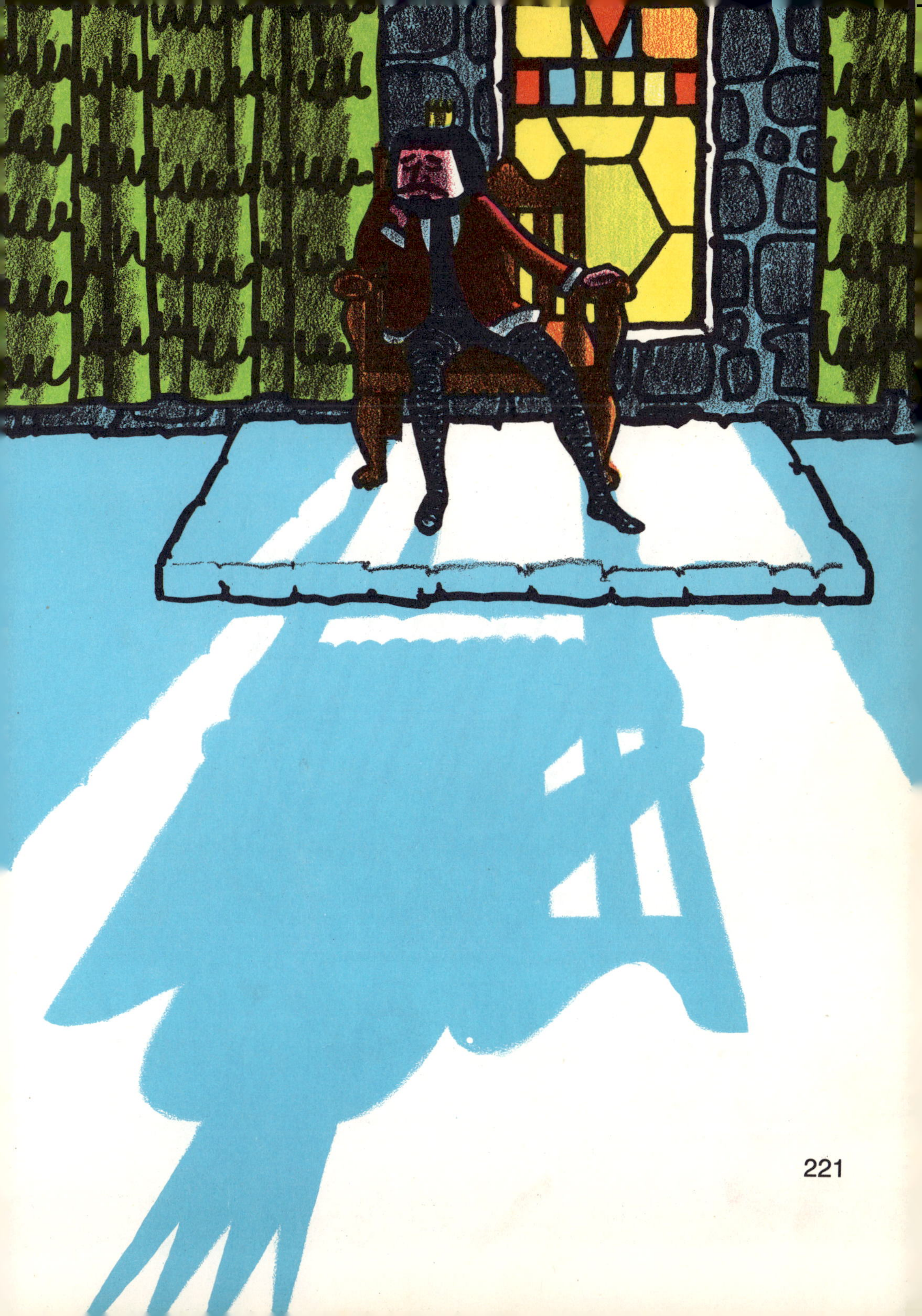

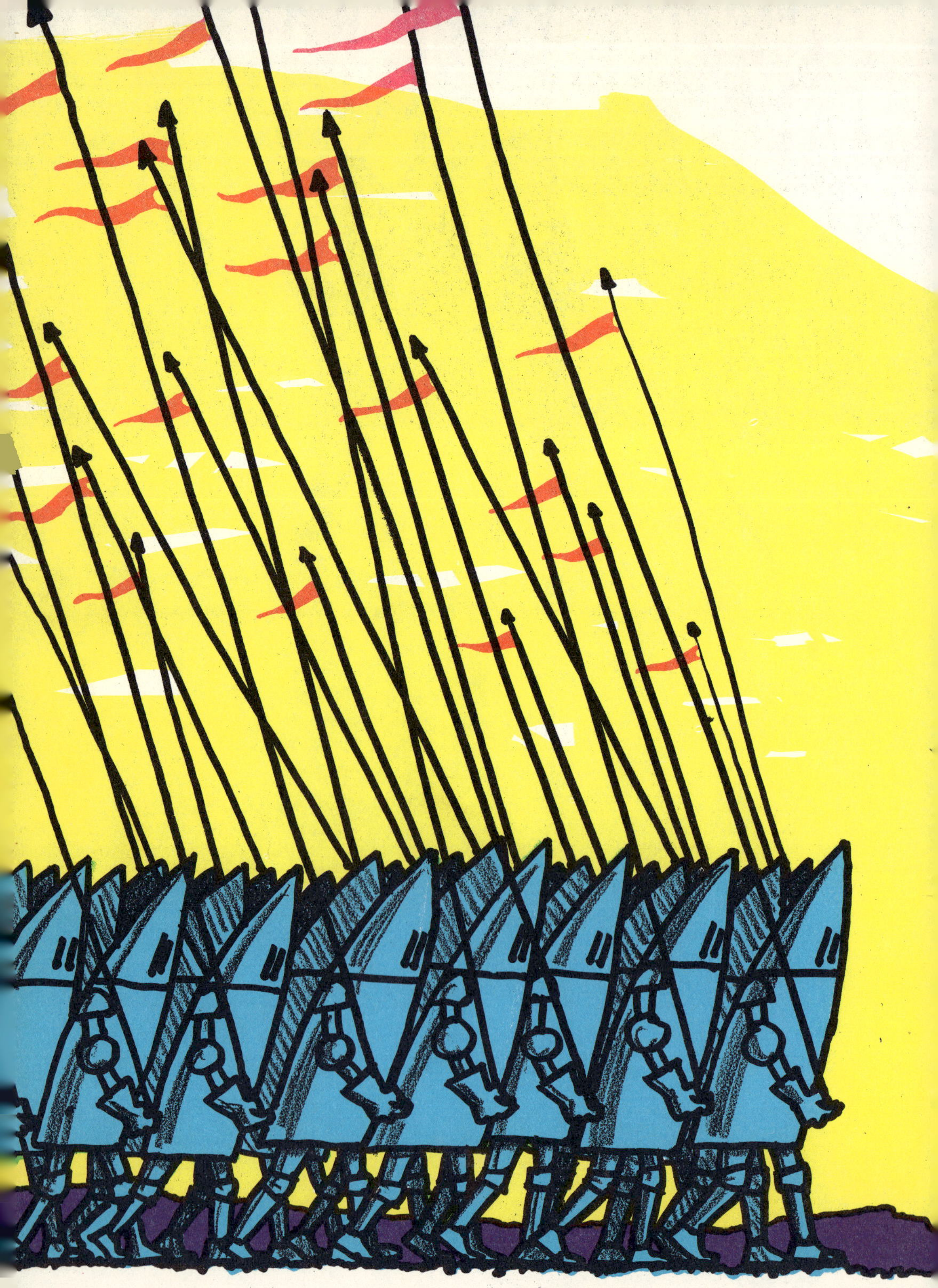

So the first thing he did was to collect money from the people of his kingdom. With the money he bought an army. With the army he set out to conquer another small kingdom not far from his own.

So determined was he to become a great king that nothing seemed to frighten him. His soldiers were inspired, and the other small kingdom was soon defeated. From this kingdom he took all the precious things he could find. There were so many that he had to add a special room, for his small castle would not hold them all.

In honor
of his victory
he had a new piece
added
to his crown
and a splendid
new robe made,
which he wore
over his old one
to remind him
of how unimportant
he used to be.
Of course,
he was so busy
taking care of
his new things that
he no longer had time
to visit his people,
hardly ever
spoke to his friends,
and seldom told
his daughter a story.

The next thing he did was to buy a navy and another army with which he set out to conquer another kingdom.

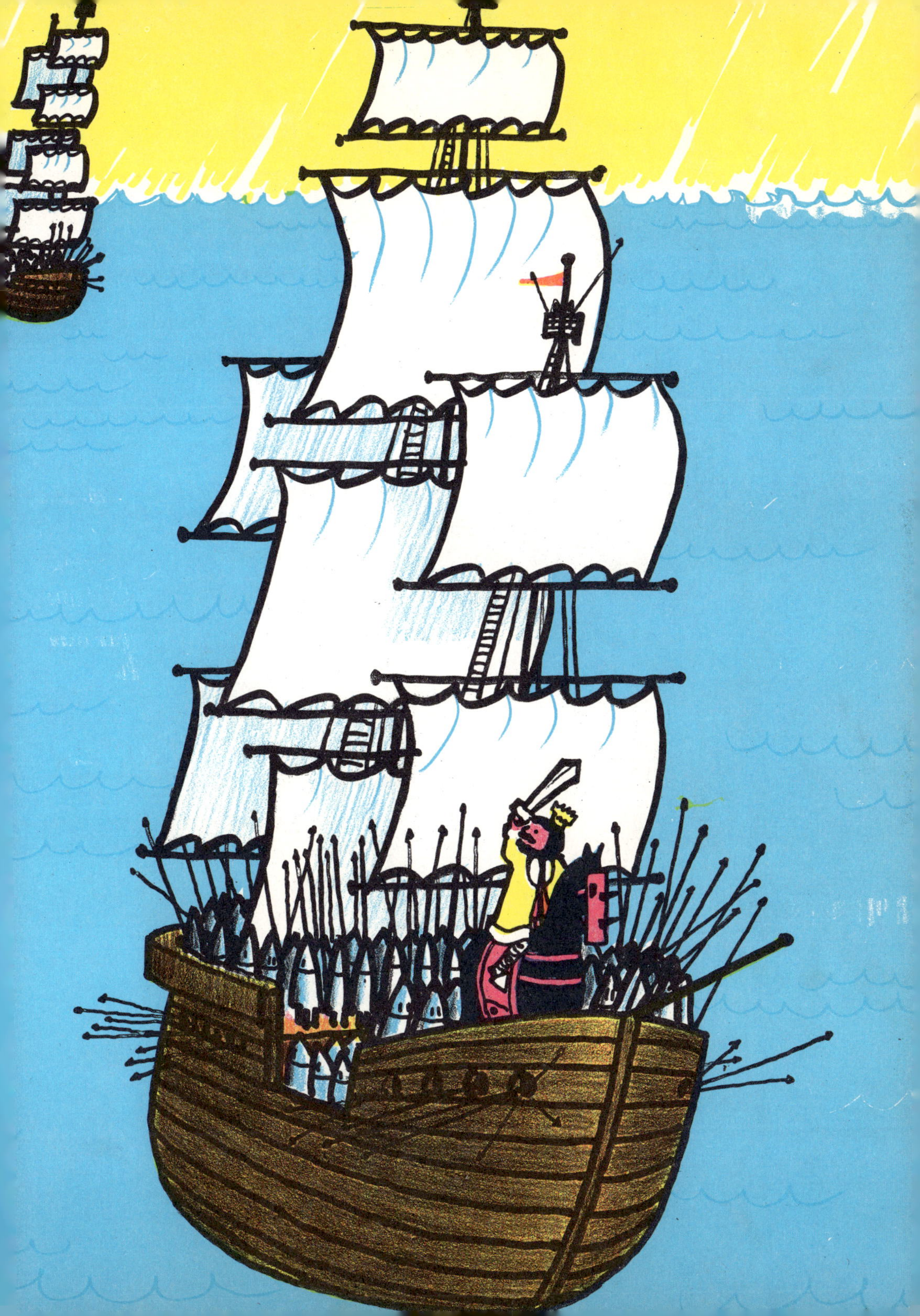

His soldiers and sailors were inspired by his bravery, and the second kingdom was soon defeated. He tore down its buildings and took all of its treasures. There were so many that he had to add more rooms to hold them all.

In honor
of this victory
he had
another piece
added to his crown
and an even more
splendid robe made,
which he wore
over his others
to remind him
of how unimportant
he used to be.
Now he never
visited his people
or spoke to his friends
and hardly ever
had a moment
to spend
with his daughter.
He was
much too busy
becoming a great king.

He bought larger armies and led them against larger kingdoms. One after another they fell to his legions. Even the great kingdom across the sea, from which the visitor came, proved no match against his bravery. From all these kingdoms he took so many precious things that . . .

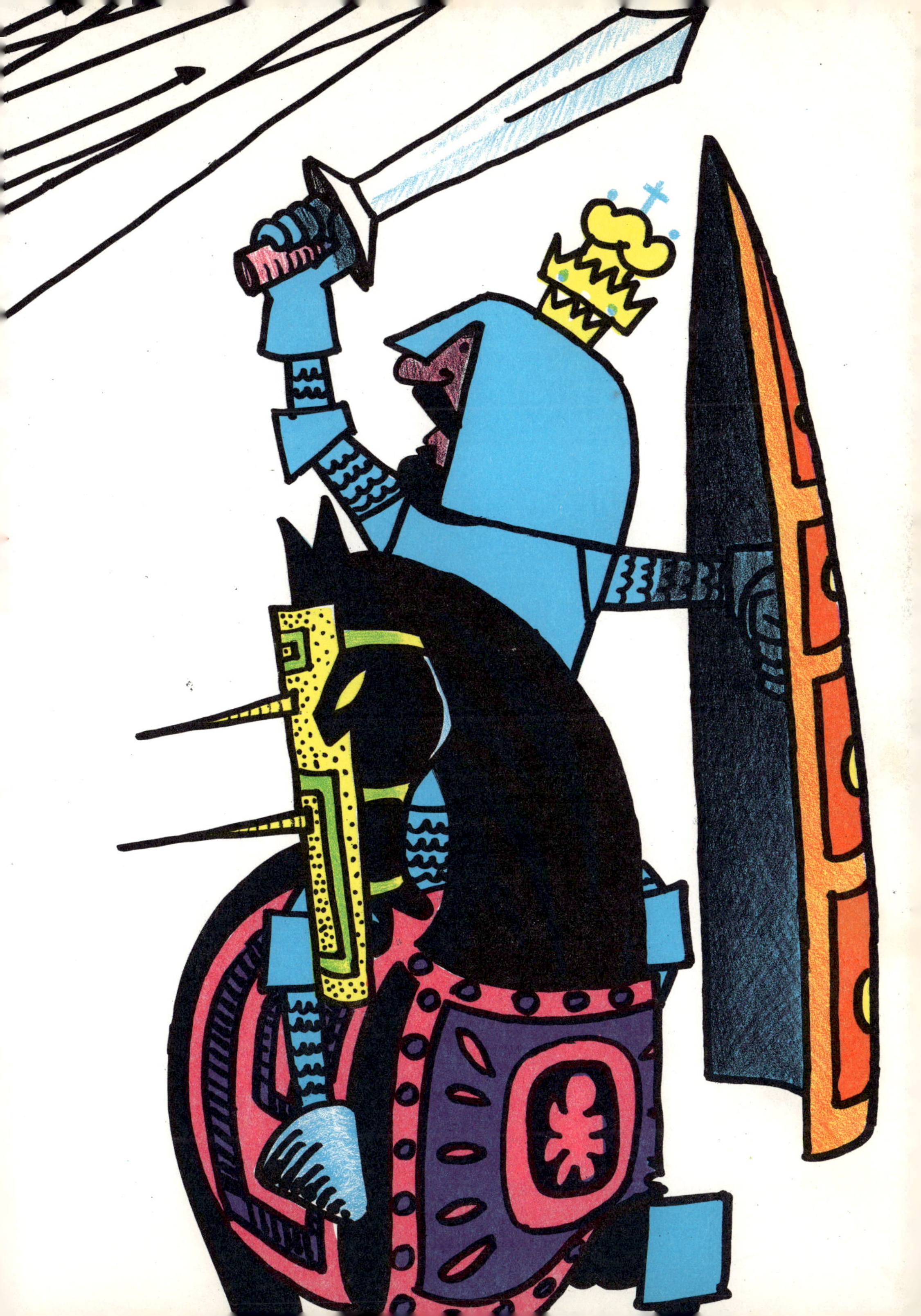

. . . he
had
to
add
more
and
more
rooms
until
his
castle
reached
way
up
into
the
clouds.

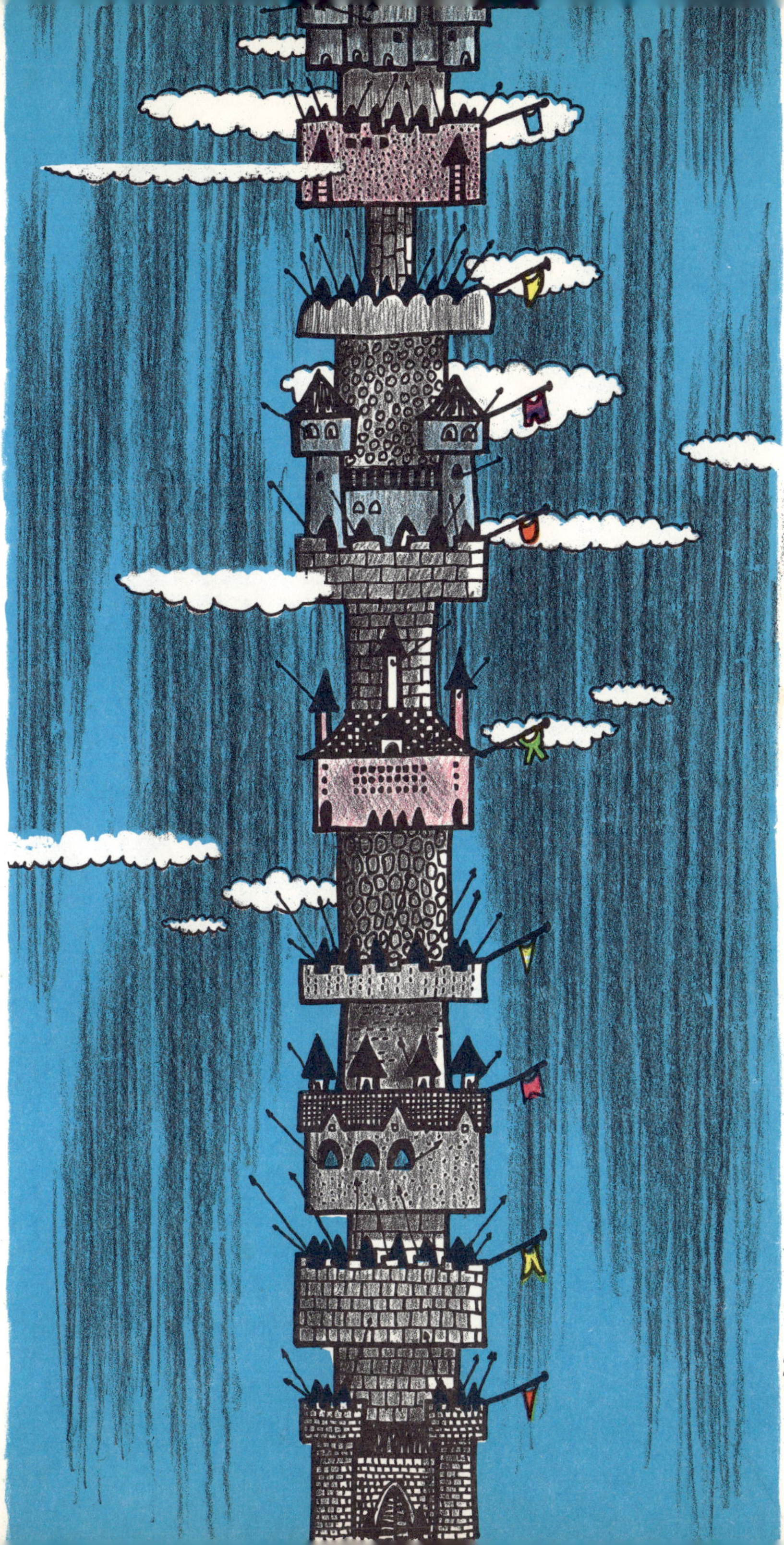

After each victory
his crown
grew
taller
and
grander,
and his robes
became
ever
more
magnificent.
And
he wore
each
finer
robe
over
his
others
to remind him . . .
of how unimportant
he used to be.

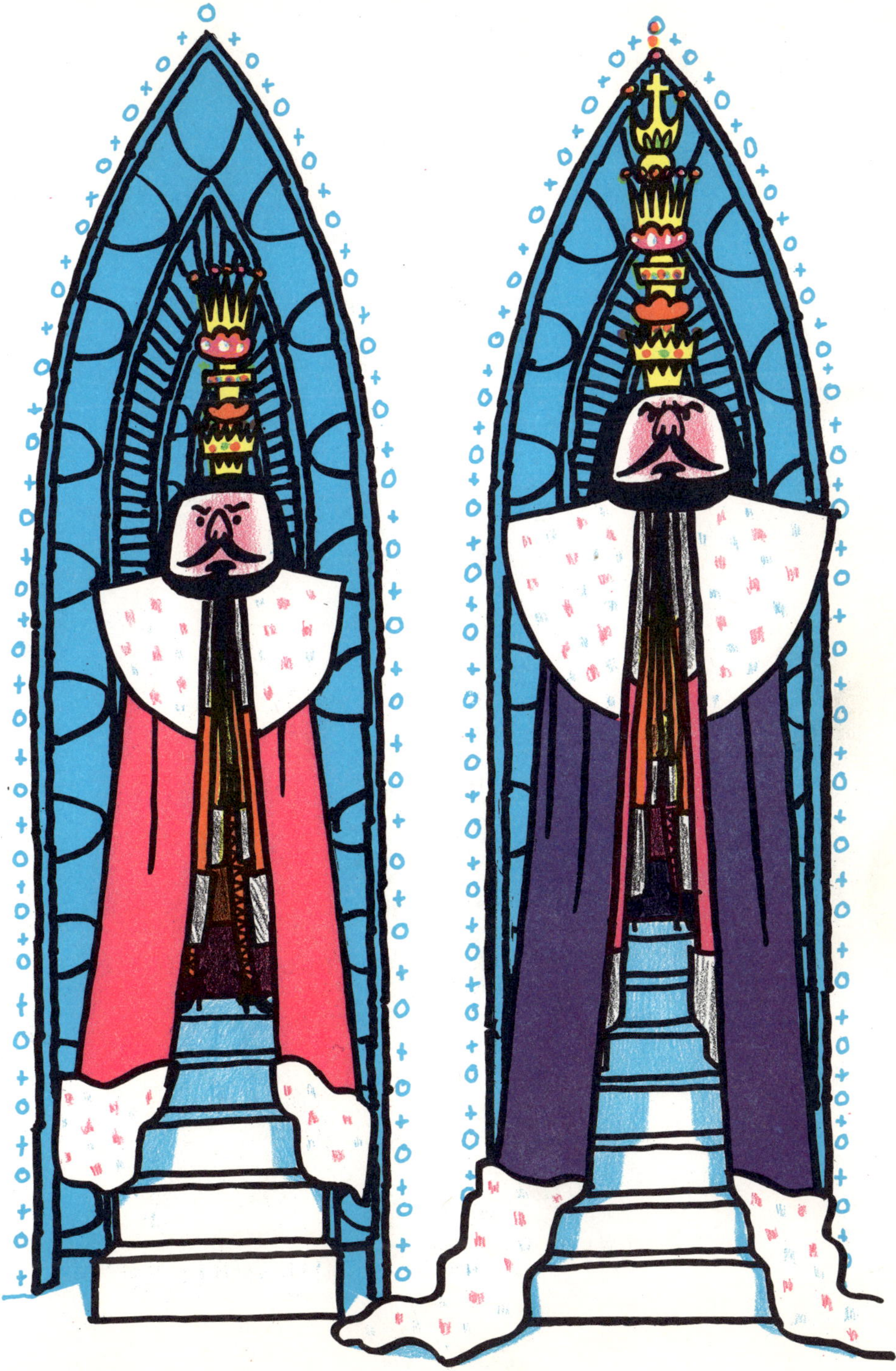

Of course, by this time he had become so great a king that he never visited his people or spoke to his friends and never had a minute to spend with his very own daughter. And though she had a governess, fourteen tutors, and sixty-three servants to see to her slightest whim, she missed him terribly.

But the great king was too busy taking care of kingly things to notice.

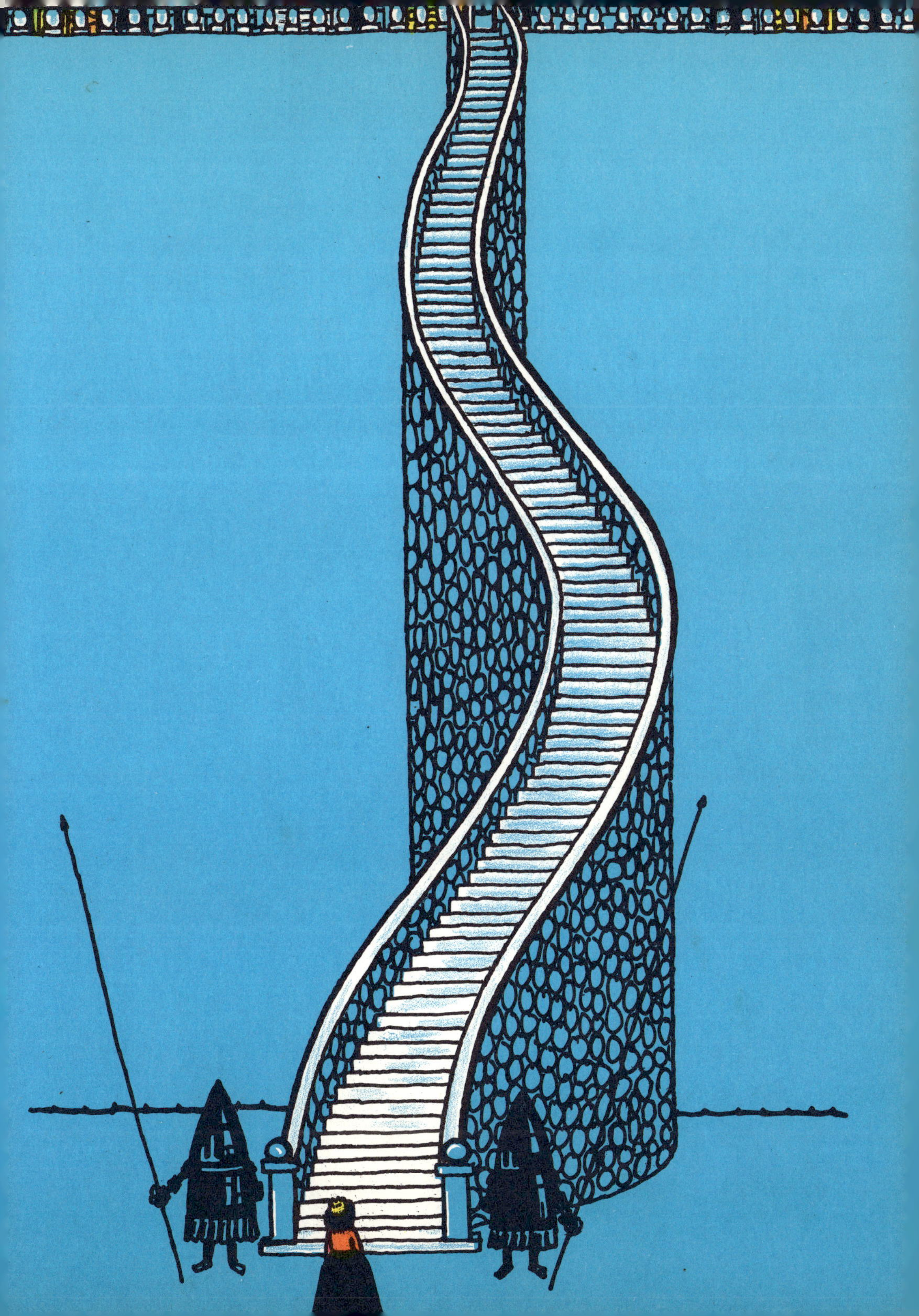

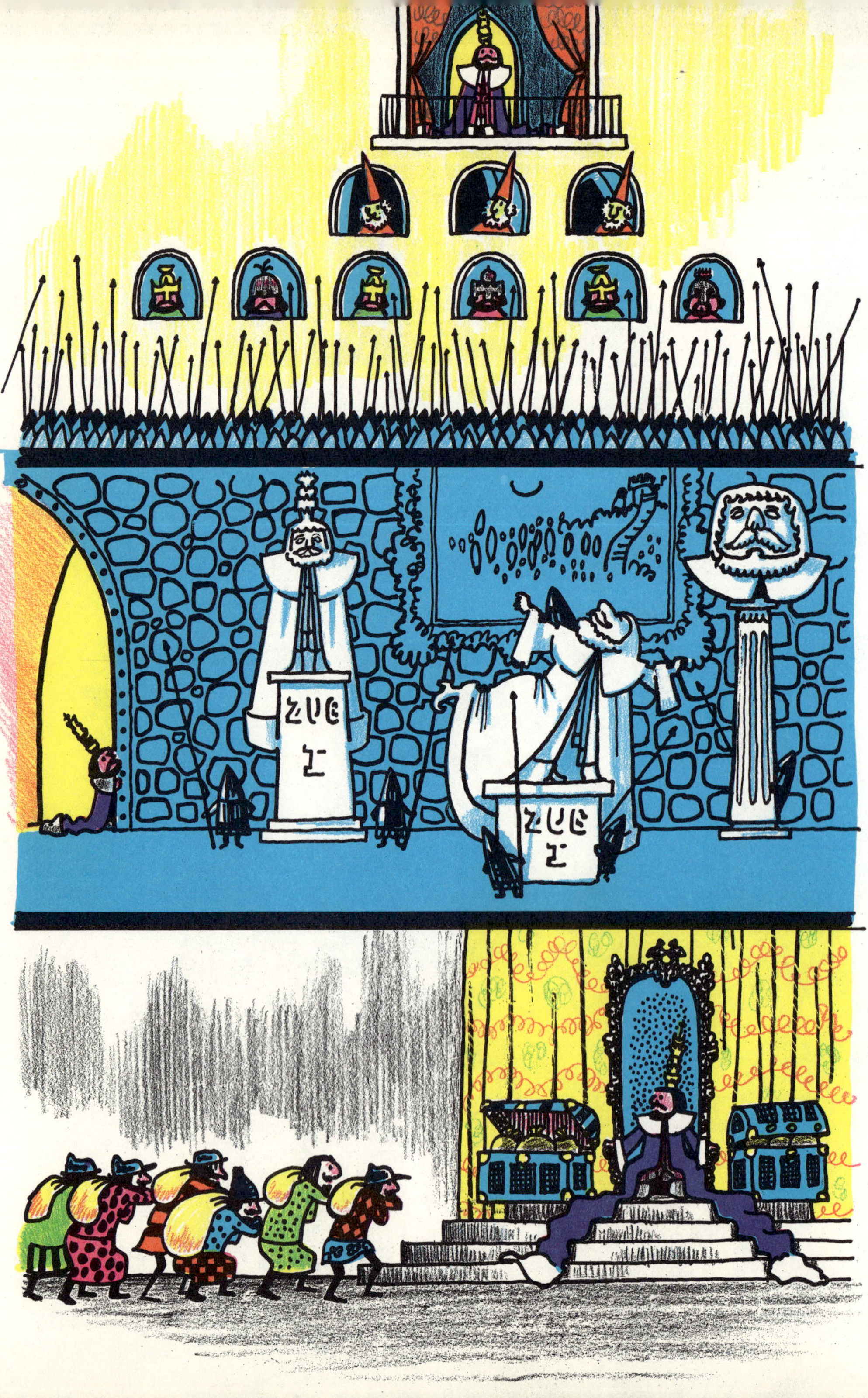
ZUG
I
ZUG
I

He had thousands of soldiers to protect his kingdom. He had captains to lead the soldiers, generals to lead the captains, and several prime ministers to watch out for things that might happen.

And over all of them the great king busily commanded.

He had guards to guard his treasures, special guards to watch the guards who watched his treasures, and extra-special guards to watch the special guards who watched the guards who guarded all his treasures.

And over all of them he busily watched to see that nothing was stolen.

He had collectors who collected money from all his people and other collectors who collected from these collectors and gave the money to the central collectors.

And from all and every one of them he busily collected.

And every day he walked up all his stairs, stopping at each storeroom on the way, in order to count his treasures. When he reached the very top of his tower, he would go out on the balcony from which he could see his entire kingdom. There he would strut back and forth like a proud peacock, and in his loudest, most kinglike voice, he would roar:

"I have pictures on each wall.
I have statues in each hall.
I have extra-fancy chairs.
I have rugs on floors and stairs.
I own carriages and boats.
I have diamonds on my coats.
I have shoes of finest leathers.
All my pillows have goose feathers.
All my shirts are made of silk.
I have nine hundred sixty-two
    vitamins in my milk.
I have dancing, prancing horses.

All my meals have sixteen courses.
I have fifteen thousand books,
And one hundred twenty cooks.
My hunting dogs are strongest,
My splendid robe's the longest.
No one has a watch that's smaller.
No one's crown is any taller.
Now that I own all these things,
I'm the greatest king of kings."

One day, after the great king had finished shouting his poem to the sky, he leaned too far over the edge of the tower, in order to watch the changing of his guards. All at once his magnificent crown slipped from his head. The great king reached out for it frantically, for he couldn't bear to lose it, but he, too, lost his balance and began to fall.

Down, down he went. He would surely have been killed had it not been for the flagpoles from which hung the flags of all the kingdoms he had conquered.

Each of his splendid robes caught on a pole, one at a time, until, with a rip, it slipped from his back, and down he fell to the next. When the great king finally landed, he was dressed as he had been when the visitor had come from across the sea. And from each flagpole on the castle hung one of his magnificent robes!

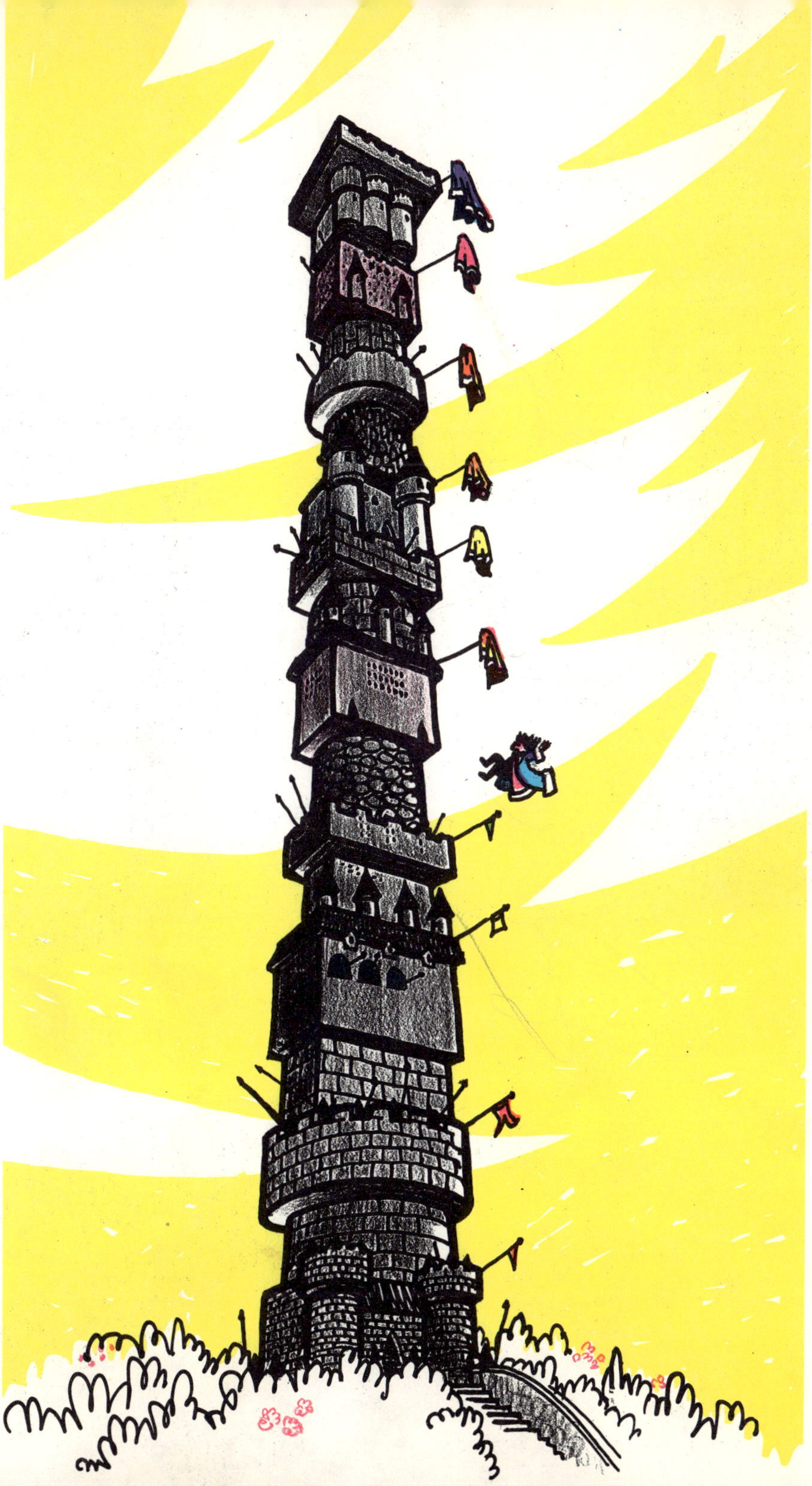

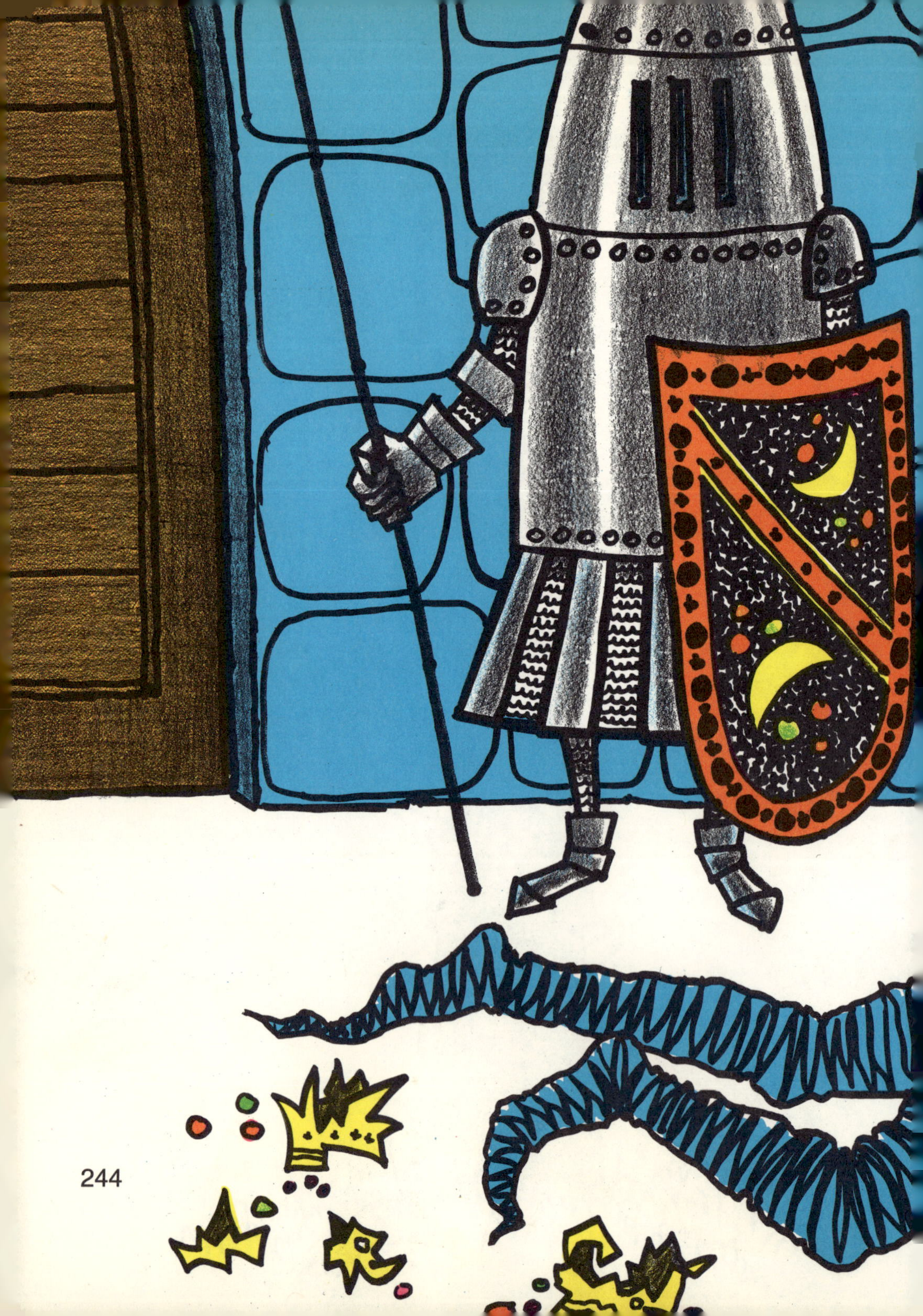

The great king lay bruised and sore. His crown was smashed to bits, his right knee was cut, and he could hardly move. Painfully he raised his head. There stood his guards at the door of his castle.

"Help me up!" he said to them.

But they didn't move. They were too busy guarding the castle and each other.

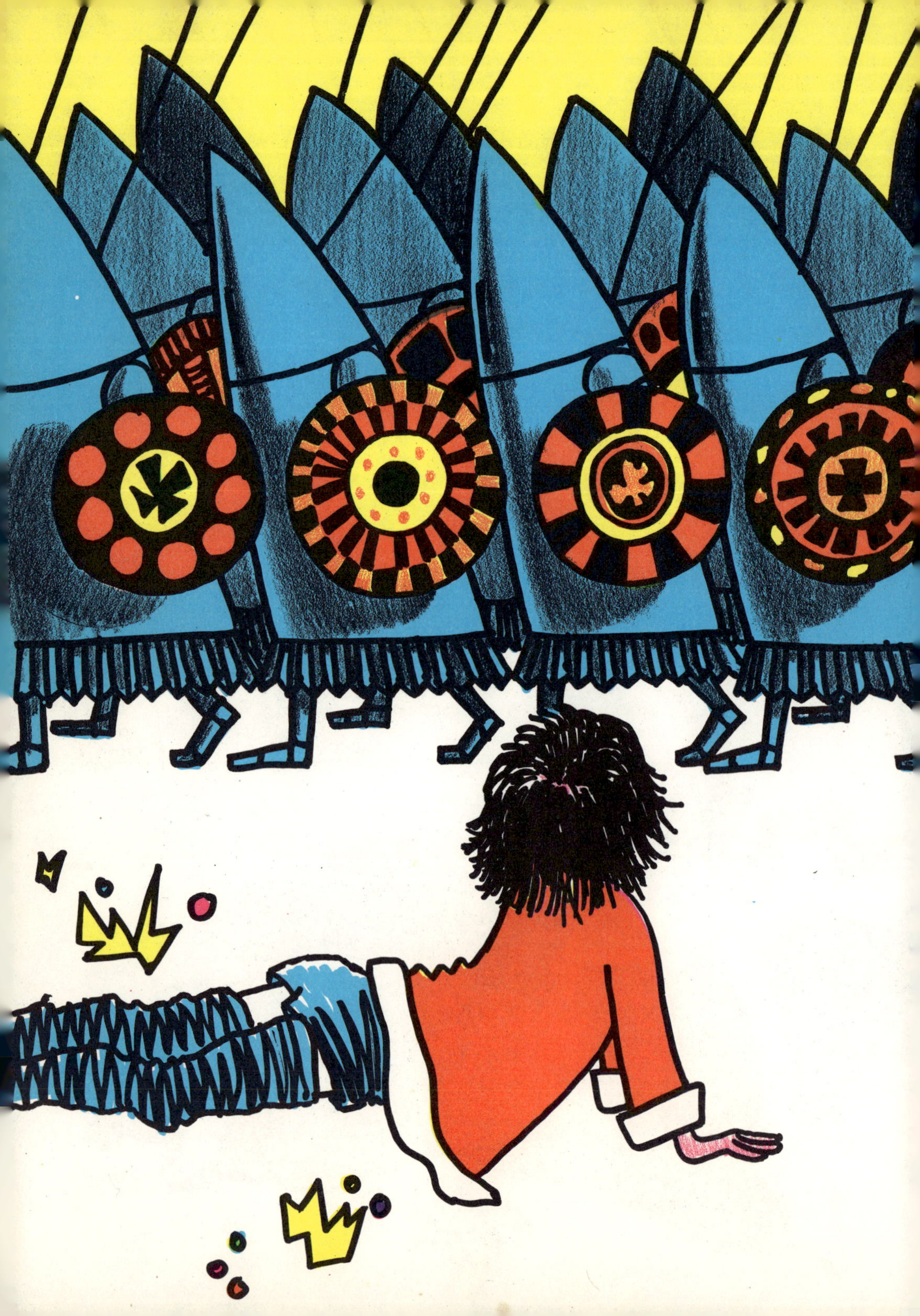

A troop of his soldiers came by on the way to a small battle.

"Help me up!" commanded the great king.

But the soldiers paid no attention.

They were too busy protecting his kingdom.

Then his collectors came by.

"Help me up!" shouted the king. "I command you!"

But they just walked right by him.

They were much too busy collecting.

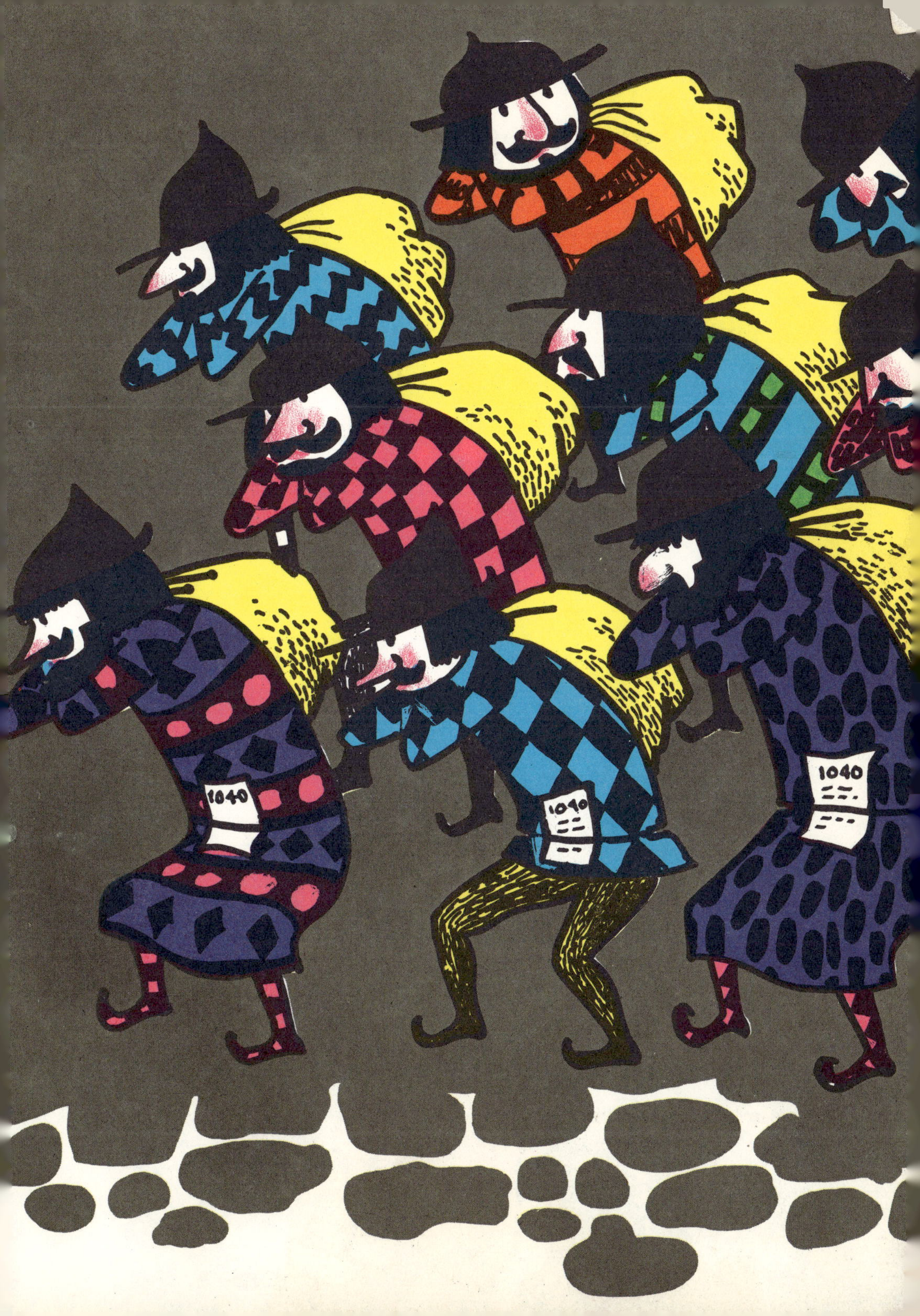
1040
1040
1040

Shortly after, his prime ministers and generals came along on their way to a most important meeting.

"Stop this minute!" he roared. "I, the greatest king on earth, command you!"

But they, too, marched right by as if he weren't even there. They were too busy prime ministering and such to stop and help him.

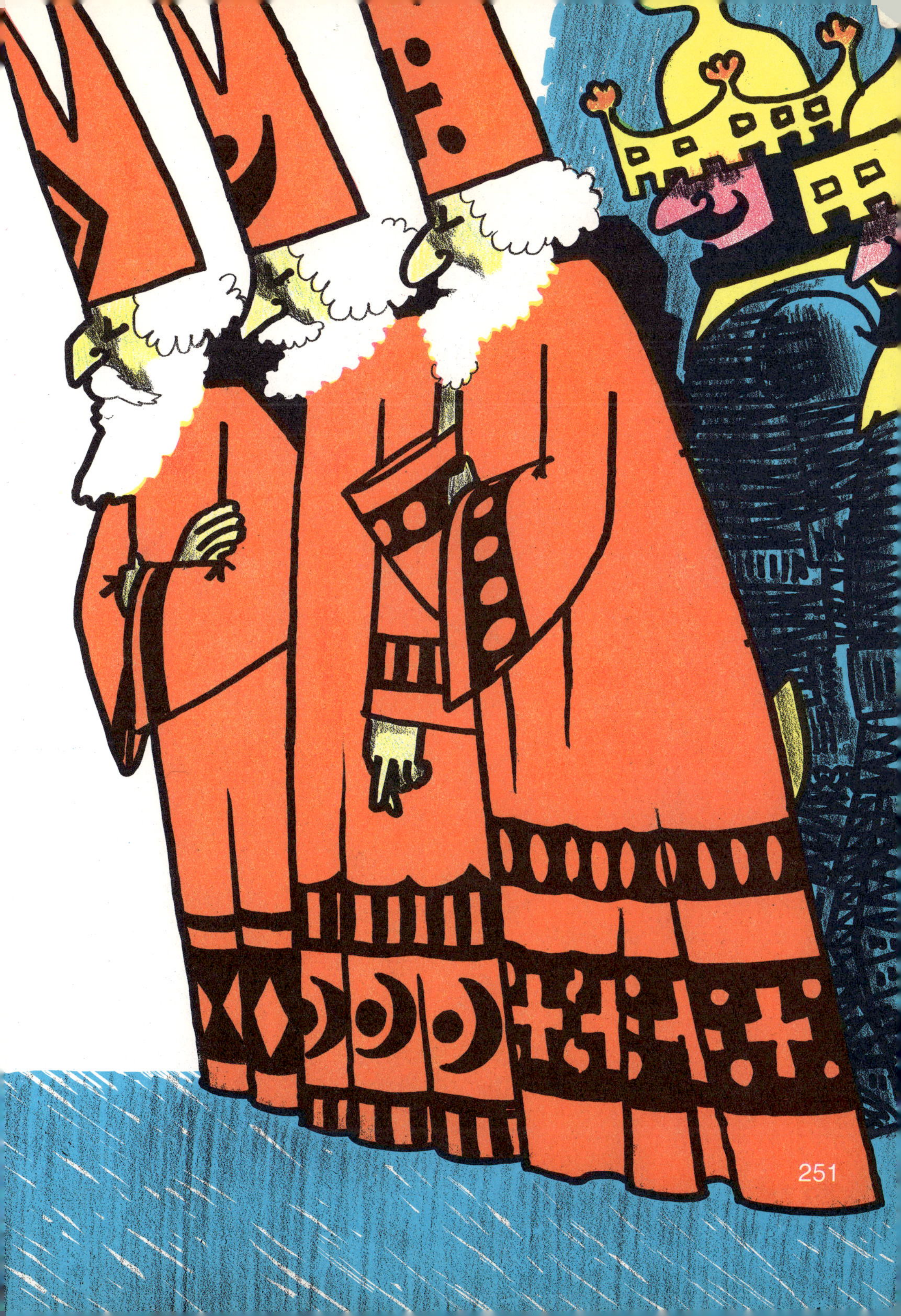

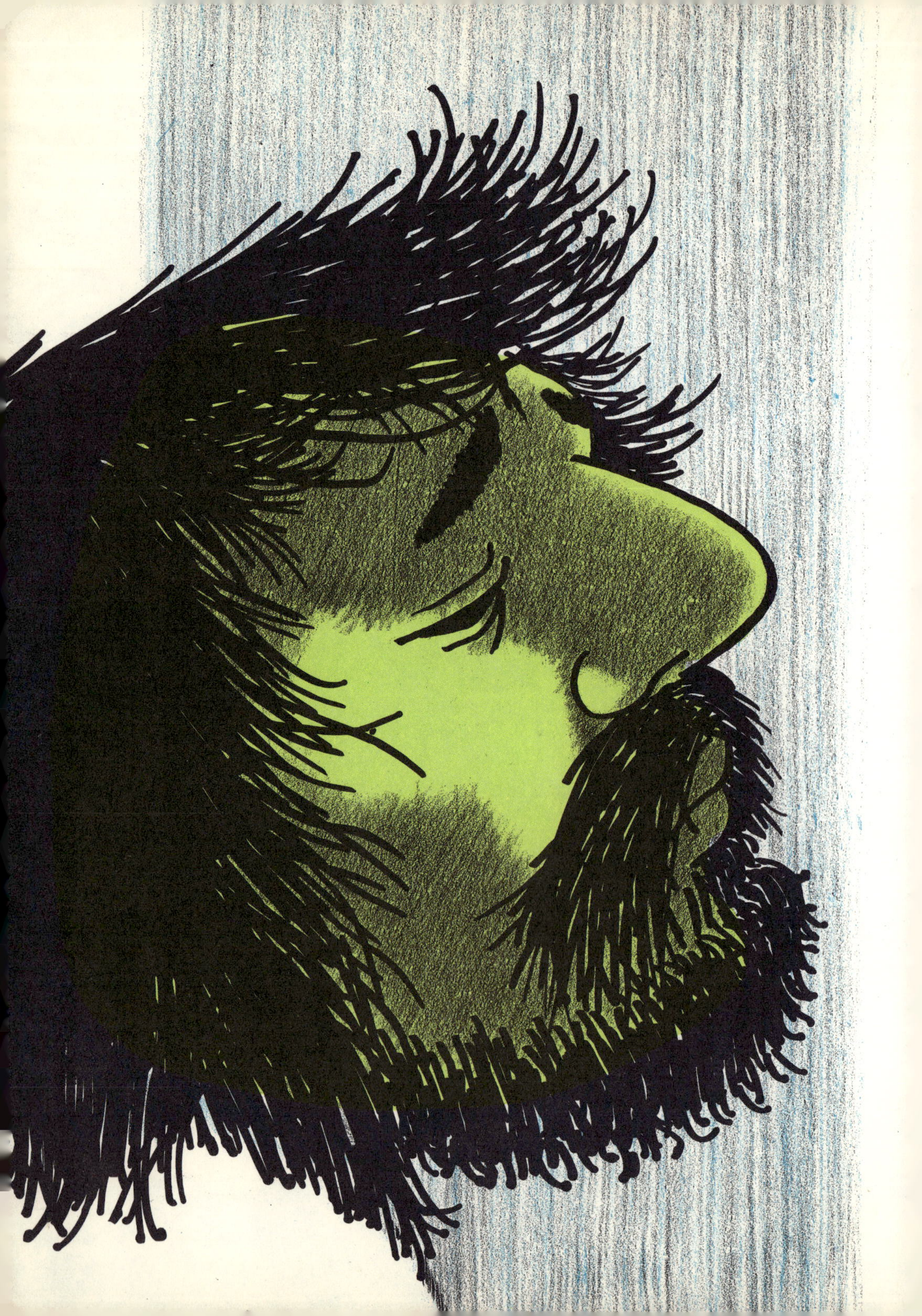

Suddenly the king realized that no one had recognized him without his grand robes and splendid crown. Besides, they were all too busy doing the things they were supposed to do. Above all, he knew in his heart that no one really cared what happened to him.

He closed his eyes. At that moment, more than jewels or gold or treasure, more than anything in the whole world, what he wanted was for someone to stop and ask, "Did you hurt yourself?"

Just then the lonely little princess, surrounded by her servants and tutors, came by on the way to her painting lesson.

She recognized the king at once.

"What happened, Father?" she asked. "Did you hurt yourself? Here, let me help you."

The little princess helped the great king to his feet.

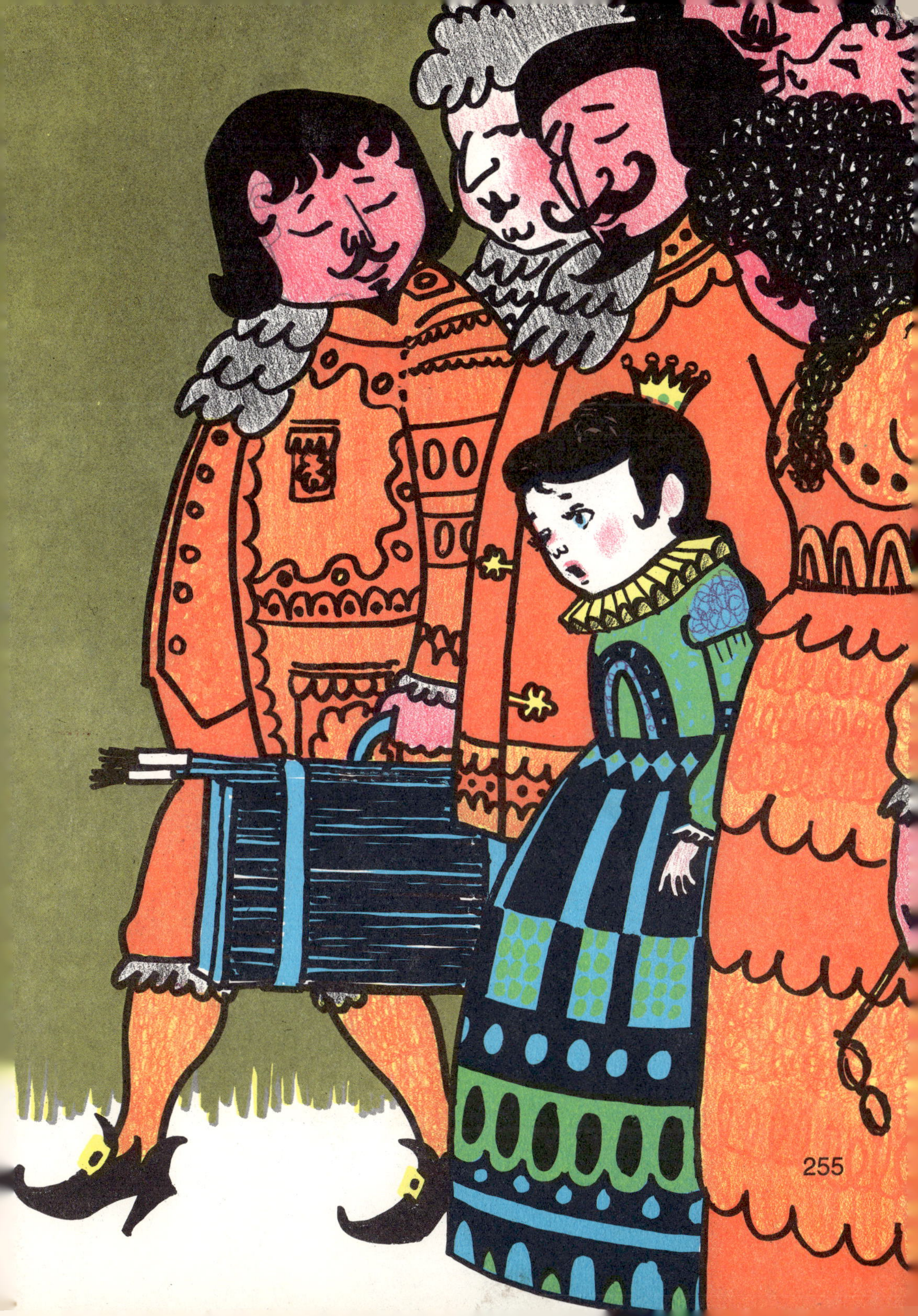

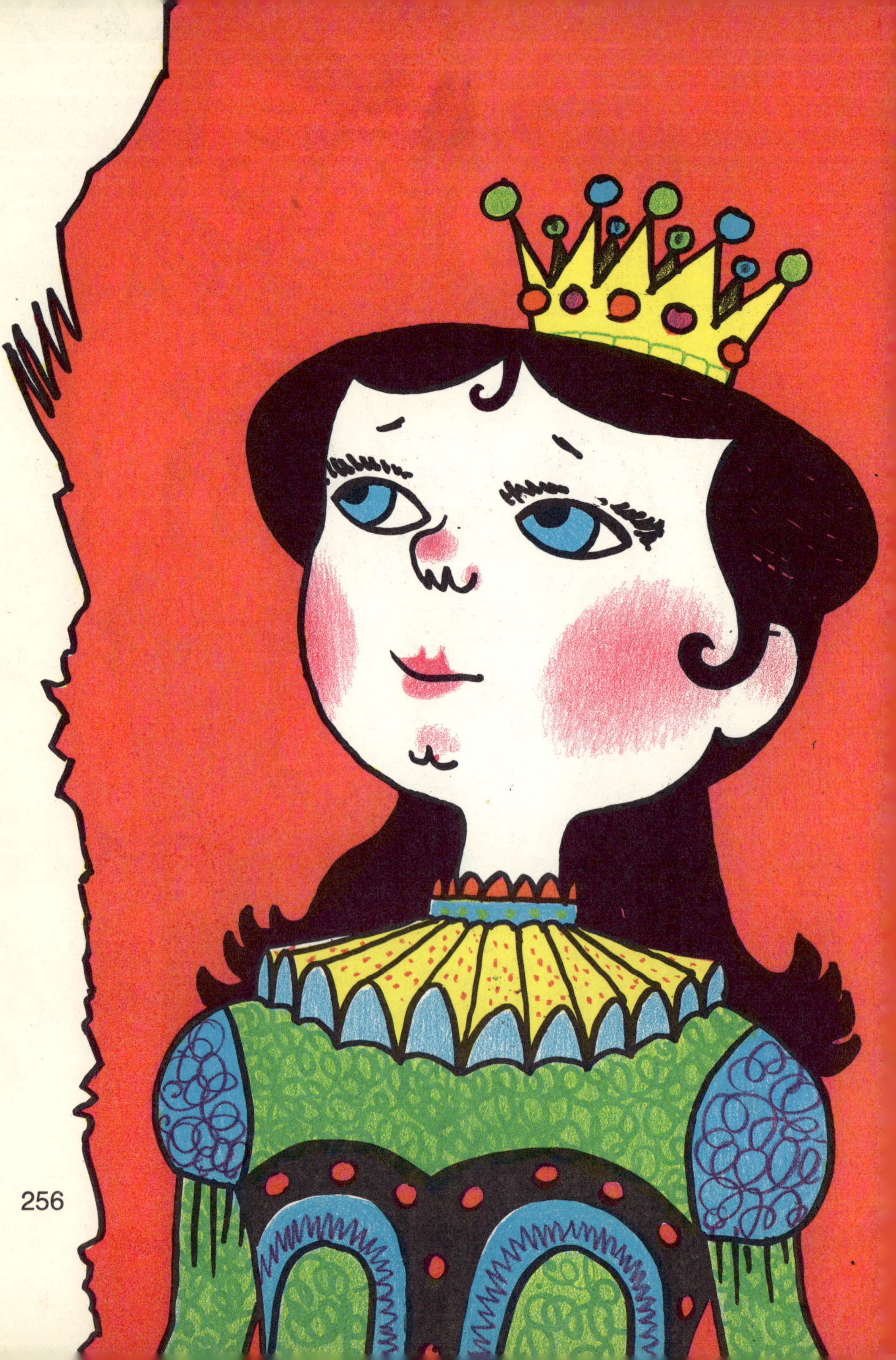

He looked down at his daughter. Her eyes seemed brighter than his brightest diamonds. Her hair seemed softer than his softest silk. She seemed more beautiful than all his treasures rolled into one.

"What a fool I was," thought the king, as they walked to the old castle. "In trying to become a great king and having all the things a great king should have, I have almost lost the most precious treasures of all — the trust of my people, the affection of my friends, and the love of my daughter. The visitor was wrong," he thought.

> "It's not great crowns that make great kings,
> Nor rooms of gold, nor diamond rings.
> More important, more by far,
> Than what we own, is what we are!"

The very next day the king returned his treasures to the kingdoms from which he had taken them. Then he dismissed his armies, navies, generals, captains, soldiers, and sailors. After that he sent away his guards, his special guards, and his extra-special guards. The collectors and the central collectors were the next to go. The only ones left were the prime ministers, and they soon followed the others.

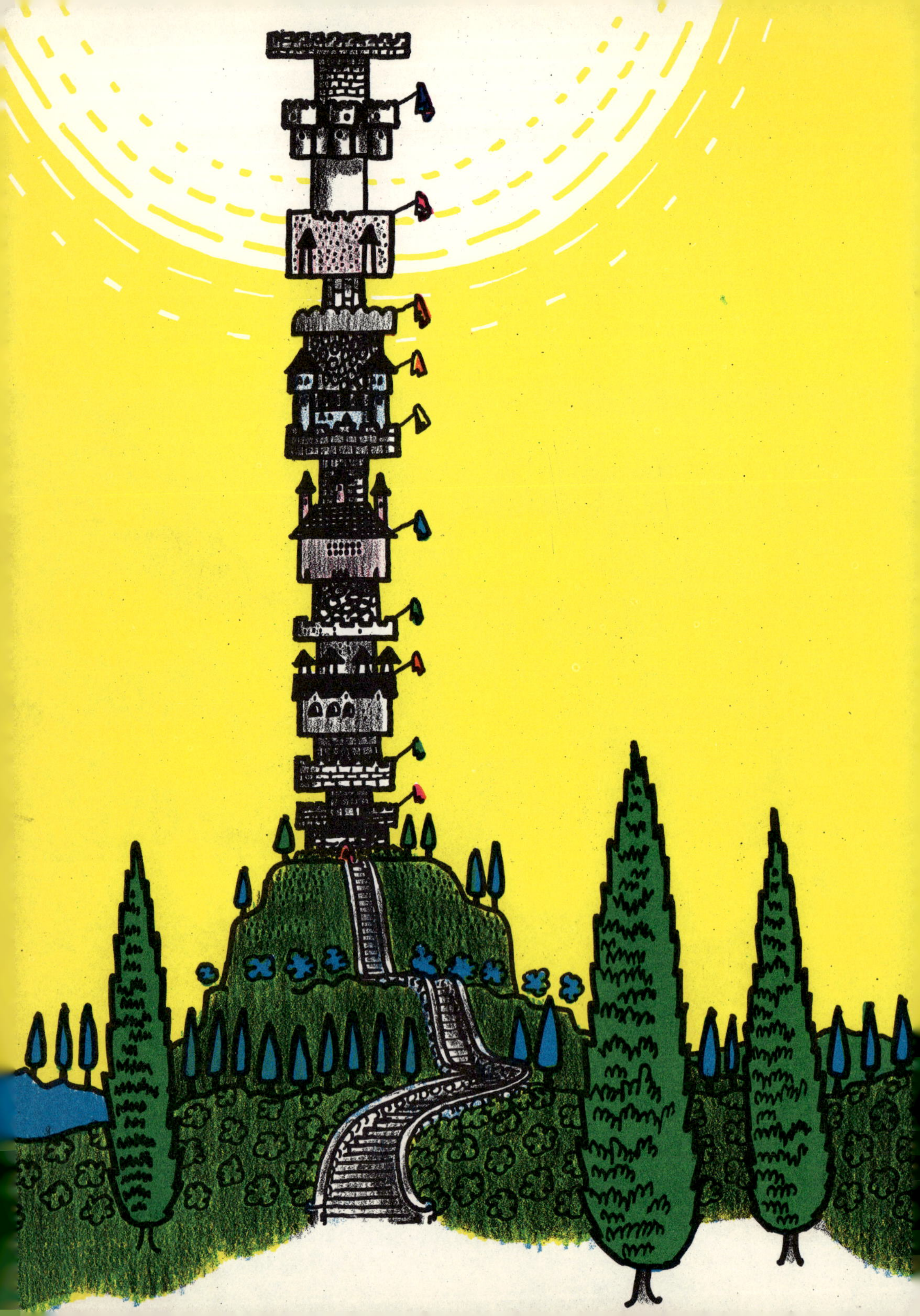

All that was left was the tall tower reaching into the sky. Though all the great rooms were now empty, the king left it standing just as it was when he fell, his grand robes hanging from each flagpole to remind him of his foolishness.

In the days that followed, when the great king would take his daughter for a walk to visit his friends and the people of his small kingdom, he would often stop for a moment to look at the tower. Then he would take his daughter's hand and give it an extra squeeze to make sure she was still there beside him.

THE END

THINKING IT OVER

Write your answers to the following questions in your notebook or on a piece of paper. Remember to number your answers.

1. What was the king too busy to do? Why was the king too busy?
2. A royal alliance is the joining of two or more kingdoms. Why did the visitor from the kingdom across the sea decide he wasn't interested in an alliance with the king?
3. Why did the king continue to wear his old robes under his new ones? Was this a good idea? Why?
4. What makes something "precious"? What did the little king learn were his most precious treasures? What are your most precious treasures?
5. Why do you think the king chose to shout his poem to the sky on pages 240–241?
6. On page 240 the author says the king

strutted like a proud peacock. What did he mean? What else could you compare the king to at this time in the story?

7. On page 219 the visitor said, "Remember this important thing: It's the crown that makes the king." Find the king's answer to that on page 257. Tell in your own words what the king meant.

TALKING IT OVER

You may want to share your ideas about these questions with others who have read *The King Who Was Too Busy*.

1. It could be said that the little king was a greater king *before* he started worrying about being great. Do you agree? Why or why not?
2. If you were in charge of making alliances with other nations, would you want the king for an ally? Why?
3. The king thought on page 241 that when

he "owned all these things" he was the "greatest king of kings." In your opinion what makes a king a great king?

4. When did the king learn that the crown does not make the king?

5. Do you think this story really took place? Give reasons for your answer.

COMPLETE THE SENTENCES

Decide how to complete the following sentences. Then write them in your notebook or on a piece of paper.

1. When the kingdom was small, the king was _____.

    busy

    generous

    tired

2. A royal alliance is like a _____.

    marriage of kingdoms

    war between kingdoms

    separation of kingdoms

3. When the _____ left, the king felt unimportant and ashamed.

    neighboring king

    visitor

    prime minister

4. The king had become too busy to notice that his daughter _____.

    was ill

    missed him terribly

    was going to school

5. When the king fell from his tower, he was lucky to have as many _____ as he had flagpoles.

    crowns

    armies

    robes

6. The fallen king was _____ by everyone who saw him except his daughter.

    kicked

    helped

    overlooked

7. The king got rid of all his possessions except his tower. He kept this as a _____.

    clothesline
    reminder
    plaything

COMPARE AND CONTRAST

You have read two stories about kings—*The Forty-Ninth Magician* and *The King Who Was Too Busy.* Think about ways in which the kings were alike and ways in which they were different. Then discuss the following questions with other *Bright Horizons* readers.

1. How did each king find happiness?
2. How did visitors play important roles in *The King Who Was Too Busy* and *The Forty-Ninth Magician?*
3. Which king did you feel you understood better as a person? Why?

4. In today's world could a real king do the things the kings in these stories did?
5. Which story did you like better? Give reasons for your answer.
6. Do you know the story of King Midas? Would you say King Midas was more like the king who was too busy or the king in *The Forty-Ninth Magician?*

LOOKING AT PICTURES

1. Look at the pictures on pages 234–235. How has the artist led you to think that the king has grown taller? Why did he do this?
2. Look at the picture on page 252. How would you describe the king and his feelings as the artist has drawn him?
3. On page 249, there are 1040 forms in the pockets of the king's collectors. Do you know what 1040 forms are? If not, ask a grown-up.

REAL OR MAKE-BELIEVE?

In your notebook or on a piece of paper, write the sentences from below which would *only* be found in a make-believe story.

Once there was a little king who ruled a small kingdom far away in a small land.

The gentle king bought armies and navies and conquered many kingdoms in a short time.

The king had to add more and more rooms until his castle reached way up into the clouds.

The king fell from his tall tower. He was only bruised and sore.

The king realized his daughter meant more to him than riches.

THE KING OF UMPALAZZO
by Mary Ann Hoberman

O the King of Umpalazzo
Is very big and fat;
He eats raw steak and chocolate cake
And grouse and mouse and rat,
And veal and eel and Hudson seal
And cracker meal and lemon peel
And dogs that bark and pigs that squeal;
What *do* you think of that?

O the King of Umpalazzo
Is very, very old;
His beard is long and yellow;
His feet are always cold.
His face is full of wrinkles;
His eyesight is quite dim;
He's a silly old billy
Who's always too chilly;
What *do* you think of him?

Copyright © 1959 by Mary Ann and Norman Hoberman. From HELLO AND GOOD BY by Mary Ann Hoberman, by permission of Little, Brown and Co.

O the King of Umpalazzo
Is very, very nice;
He says "I thank you" once a day
And he says "you're welcome" twice.
He nods his head and tips his hat
And shakes your hand and walks his cat.
He never tells you not to speak
And he gives out ice cream every week.
He's a funny old honey,
As soft as a bunny;
What *do* you think
     What *do* you think
          What *do* you think of that?

The poet asks what you think of the King of Umpalazzo. How do you think she feels about him?

IF I WERE KING
by A. A. Milne

I often wish I were a King,
And then I could do anything.

If only I were King of Spain,
I'd take my hat off in the rain.

If only I were King of France,
I wouldn't brush my hair for aunts.

I think, if I were King of Greece,
I'd push things off the mantelpiece.

If I were King of Norroway,
I'd ask an elephant to stay.

If I were King of Babylon,
I'd leave my button gloves undone.

If I were King of Timbuctoo,
I'd think of lovely things to do.

If I were King of anything,
I'd tell the soldiers, "I'm the King!"

From the book WHEN WE WERE VERY YOUNG by A. A. Milne. Copyright, 1924, by E. P. Dutton & Co., Inc. Renewal, 1952, by A. A. Milne. Reprinted by permission of E. P. Dutton & Co., Inc. and Associated Book Publishers Ltd.

COLLECTORS' ITEMS

THE FOOLING OF KING ALEXANDER
by Mervyn Skipper

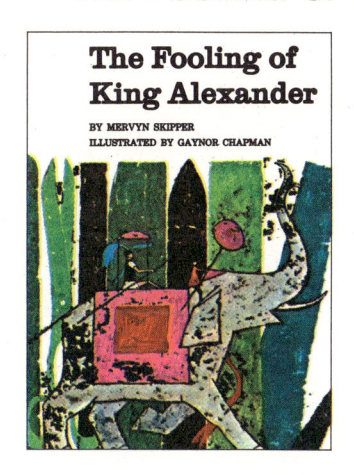

Alexander was a powerful king. When the Emperor of China heard that King Alexander planned to conquer China, he called in his wise men. But it was a small serving boy who saved the country.

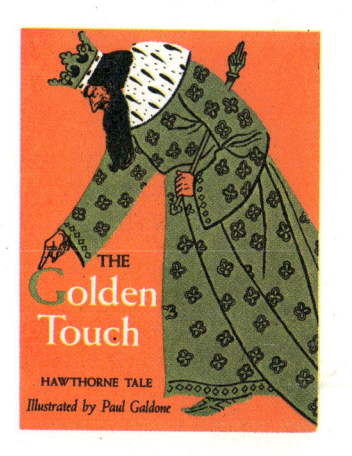

THE GOLDEN TOUCH
by Nathaniel Hawthorne

What more could the king ask than to have the power to turn into gold everything that he touched?

ONCE UPON A MOUNTAIN
by Don Bolognese

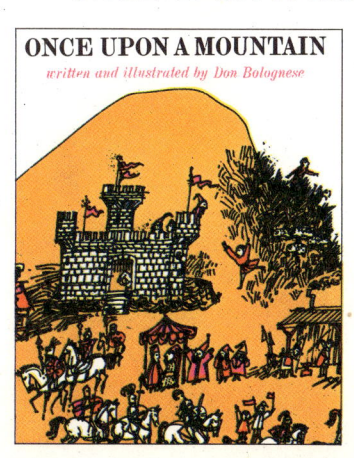

A lonely shepherd boy playfully calls for help from one mountain to another. When laughter comes back, he sounds the alarm. What happens next will remind you of the boy in Aesop's fable who cried wolf.

After many hours of bargaining, the sheik bought nine handsome camels—dark tobacco-colored camels, golden ginger-colored camels, and some creamy white camels.

"Amin, you are an honest man. I am going to let you take these beautiful camels back to our camp," said the sheik. "But take care. Take care not to lose any of our nine camels."

انتبه كي لا نفقد واحدا من جمالنا

ANN KIRN grew up in Missouri and graduated from Columbia University in New York City. She is both an artist and an author.

Miss Kirn wanted the pictures in *Nine in a Line* to look like the Arabic paintings in old books. She studied many old Arabic paintings before doing the illustrations.

Miss Kirn writes, "The story came from the familiar plot of an old folk tale, which I thought was amusing and hoped children would chuckle over."

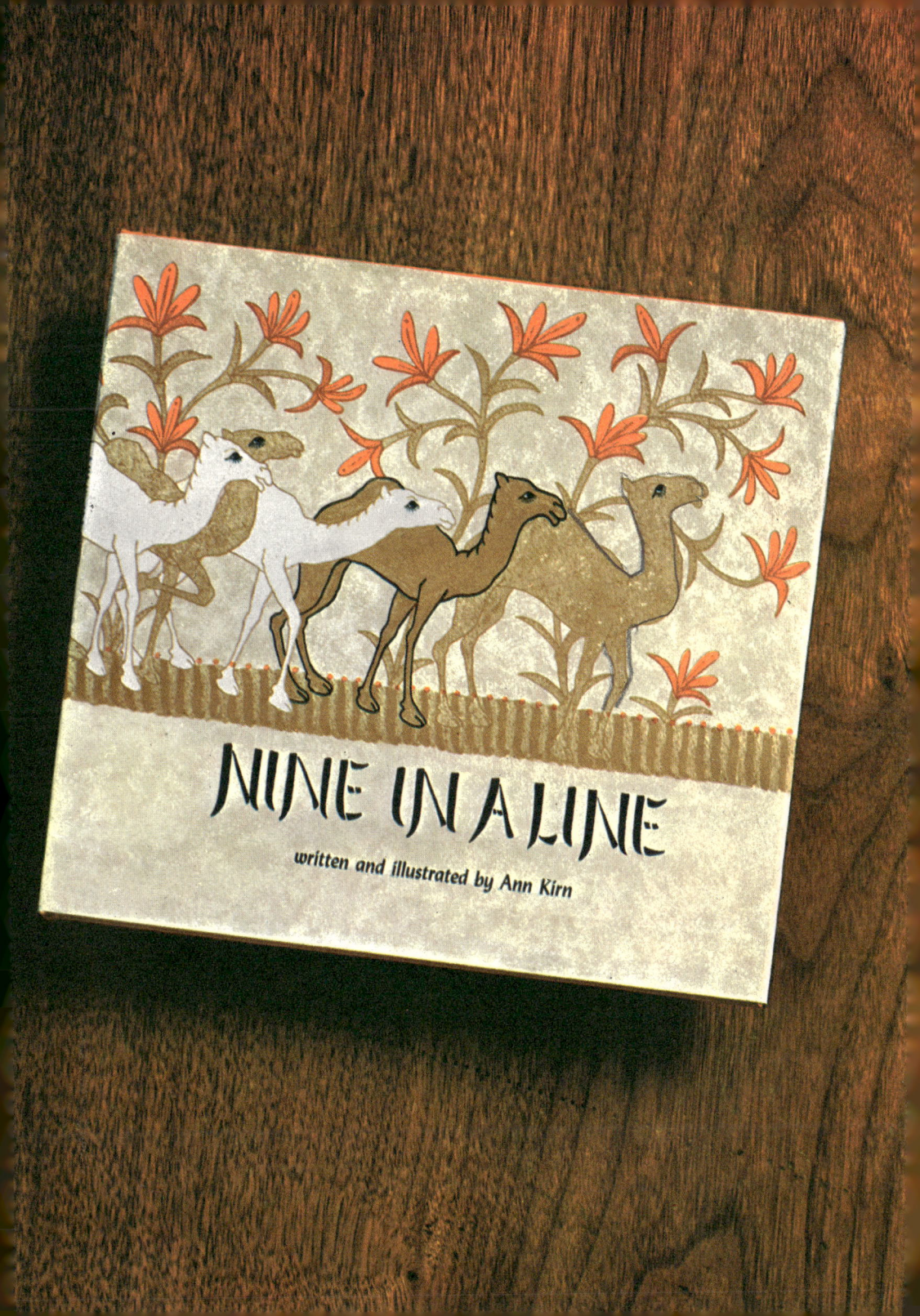

NINE IN A LINE

written and illustrated by Ann Kirn

Amin is an Arab living in Arabia. He is given an important job by the leader of his tribe. Amin wants very much to do his job well. Will the Evil One keep him from carrying out his task?

NINE IN A LINE

FROM AN OLD, OLD FOLKTALE

written and illustrated by
Ann Kirn

Arabic by Leila Leonard

W · W · Norton & Company · Inc · New York

LOVELL J. HONISS SCHOOL
DUMONT, NEW JERSEY

Reprinted from NINE IN A LINE, From An Old, Old Folktale
Written and illustrated by Ann Kirn. Arabic by Leila Leonard
By permission of W. W. Norton & Company, Inc.
Copyright © 1966 by Ann Kirn

الشيخ و أمين توجها إلى سوق الجمال

"Nine camels. Our Bedouin tribe needs nine healthy camels to add to our caravan," said the sheik to Amin.

They were on their way to the camel market. The tall sheik walked proudly through the streets, stretching his long legs a little farther with each step.

Amin tripped along behind.

Amin was a dumpy little man with a very long nose, black twinkly eyes, and a curly mouth. When Amin smiled, his wide mouth turned up like a quarter moon.

مئات من الجمال يملؤن السوق

The sheik and Amin soon arrived at the market place. They looked around and saw two hundred, maybe three hundred, camels crowded together with their masters.

"Look them over carefully. Look them over well," urged the sheik.

"Yes, yes," murmured Amin, "we want only the best."

They looked. They punched and poked. They rejected. They chose.

"I'll be careful, very careful," promised Amin.

Amin lined up the camels, one after another, like toy soldiers.

He went down the line counting, "1 — 2 — 3 — 4 — 5 — 6 — 7 — 8 — 9 camels. They are all here. I am ready to start."

تمشى الجمال متخترةً في الصحراء الرملية

Amin gave a deep grunt to one of the ginger-colored camels to make him kneel. He slipped a bridle over his nose. Then Amin clambered up onto the kneeling camel's hump, and the camel rose, stiff-legged.

Out into the wide sandy desert stalked the line of camels — nose to tail, tail to nose.

Amin, rocking backward, then forward,
sang to himself,
"Take care, take care,
There are nine in the line."

Suddenly, he stopped singing and shouted, "Oh woe! The sheik forgot to buy blue beads for the camels. Now there is nothing to frighten away the Evil One."

His coal-black eyes lost some of their twinkle. His wide mouth lost some of its curl. He began to worry, worry, worry.

"No blue beads. *No blue beads*," he worried. "The Evil One will come and grab the camels. He has probably made off with one of them already."

He turned himself around on the hump and, riding backwards, he counted, "1—2—3—4—5—6—7—8. *Eight!* Only eight camels. Oh woe! Woe! The Evil One has taken a camel!"

أمين يعد الجمال واحداً واحداً

أمين يركض نحو الراعي الذي يخيم بين شقائق الأقحوان

He stopped the lead camel and slid down its thick tail to the ground. He stooped over to count camel tracks. There were too many. They were too mixed-up.

"Where, oh where, did the Evil One take our camel?" he asked himself worriedly.

Amin began running fast—searching here, there, everywhere. His heart was pounding. His striped coat was ballooning out behind him.

Up and over a rocky ridge he ran. On its grass-topped dunes he saw woolly sheep grazing among the red poppies. A sunburnt shepherd sat camping by their side.

"Help me," shouted Amin. "Please help me find my lost camel. The Evil One has hidden him."

The kind shepherd left his flock to help Amin. They searched behind every bulging rock and in every cranny.

They began running round in circles, searching. And suddenly, they were back where the camels squatted, waiting for Amin.

"How many camels did you have?" asked the helpful shepherd.

"Nine camels. Nine handsome camels," answered Amin woefully.

The shepherd pointed to each camel with his crook and counted to himself.

Then he said, "Count again. Count again. There are nine in the line."

Amin counted, "1—2—3—4—5—6—7—8—9. *Nine!* All nine camels!"

His eyes widened in amazement. His mouth popped open.

He scratched his head and cried, "How come? *How come?* Just a while ago there were only eight."

"Well, you have nine camels now," said the shepherd.

Puzzled, Amin thanked the shepherd for his help.

Then the lead camel got up on his knobby knees for Amin to mount. Amin settled himself on its hump. His mouth was again curling up and his eyes twinkling, as he bid the kind shepherd farewell.

الراعي المخلص يعد الجمال

Across the endless sand they went in a clumsy camel-canter. Amin was jounced down behind the camel's hump.

He began worrying again. His heavy eyebrows wrinkled in a frown. His wide mouth drooped down.

"The Evil One. That sly old Evil One," he grumbled. "The camels need blue beads to frighten him away."

They cantered up to an oasis. A spring bubbled out of the dry sandy earth making a water hole. A few palm trees grew beside it.

امين تسلل بخفة خلف حدبة الجمل

The camels shuffled to a halt.

"I must count and check before we drink," muttered Amin.

Again he whirled around. And sitting backward on his camel, he counted, "1 — 2 — 3 — 4 — 5 — 6 — 7 — 8."

"Woe is me. *Woe Is Me!*" he moaned. "The Evil One has returned and grabbed another camel."

Amin rolled down the shaggy back of his patient camel. His head scarf fell over one eye. He straightened it and dusted himself off.

He scurried wildly about searching — sometimes shouting, sometimes sighing. But he found no camel.

Two women carrying water jars walked among the date palms.

Amin ran toward them crying, "I have lost one of my camels. Have you seen him? Have you seen my lost camel?"

"No, we haven't seen a stray camel," answered the women. "How many camels did you have?"

"I did have nine," answered Amin, "but now I have only eight. The Evil One has grabbed one of my camels."

أمين يقابل امرأتين في الواحة

أَمِين أَخَذ يَتَوَّه وِيَئِنّ

"Let us help you," said the women, and they hurried to the water hole, where the camels were lined up drinking.

Amin threw up his arms in despair. He was moaning and groaning.

The two women counted; then they shouted, "Count again. Count again. There are nine in the line."

Amin counted, "1 – 2 – 3 – 4 – 5 – 6 – 7 – 8 – 9. *Nine!* Nine camels!"

Poor Amin shook his muddled head and muttered, "I can't understand it. I just can't understand it. I counted them minutes ago, and there were only eight."

"Go your way in peace," said the women. "You have all nine camels."

The camels finished drinking, and Amin mounted his kneeling camel, still shaking his head. He was bewildered. He was befuddled.

He waved farewell to the kind women.

The camels jog-trotted across the sandy flats. Their long necks bobbed up and down, down and up.

أمين المتعجب يركب الجمل الراقد

299

The way was far. They had traveled all through the hot dusty day.

Amin looked up at the wide sky. The setting sun was sinking toward the tawny earth. Close to the rolling foothills, he saw the black goat-hair tents of his Bedouin tribe.

"I'm almost home, almost home to my house of hair," he murmured to himself. "I'll have to check the camels once more."

Amin was very tired and very puzzled. He sat hunched down in his striped coat, as he balanced on the lurching camel's hump.

But again he turned around on the hump, and his bare legs dangled on either side of the camel's scraggly tail.

خيام قبيلة السوداء ضربت تحت التلال القانية اللون

He counted the lagging camels, "1 – 2 – 3 – 4 – 5 – 6 – 7 – 8. *Eight!* Only eight camels!"

Amin stopped the camels. He rolled his eyes toward heaven. He opened wide his mouth and out poured a long drawn-out wail, "Oh woe — woe — woe — oh woe!"

The next minute three children were looking up at him and the camels.

He wailed again. And again. And again. Tears streamed down his round cheeks.

"What's wrong, Amin?" the children shouted. "Amin, are you hurt?"

"No! No, but I will hurt when the sheik finds out that I did not take care," he cried.

ثلاثة أولاد يستمعون إلى نواح أمين

"There were no blue beads to ward off the Evil One, and he has been playing tricks with the camels. Sometimes I have nine. Sometimes I have eight."

The children looked worried, "How many camels do you have now, Amin?"

"Now, I am almost home, and I have only eight!" he cried. "The sheik will beat me, beat me."

The children began to count. Amin waited, scared and silent.

Then the children whooped and hollered, "Nine! *Nine!* There are nine in the line!"

Amin counted very slowly, taking great care to point to each camel, "One camel, two camels, three camels, four camels, five camels, six camels, seven camels, eight camels."

"I count only eight," he muttered, shaking his head.

ألا ولاد ينبهون أمين على غلطه

"Oh Amin, Amin, you forgot to count the camel you are sitting on!" laughed the children.

Amin threw up his hands, his black eyes danced, his mouth curled up in a wide grin.

He shouted, "What a *silly* I am! Don't tell anyone what an old silly I am."

الأولاد مع أمين يفحكون ـ وية

Afterward, whenever the children met Amin, they chanted,
"Eight or nine
In the line."
And Amin and the children had a big secret laugh.

THINKING IT OVER

Write your answers to these questions in your notebook or on a piece of paper. Remember to number your answers.

1. Why do you think the author chose the title *Nine in a Line*? Can you think of some other titles she might have used?
2. Who is the main character in this folk tale? Who are some of the other characters? Could the Evil One be considered a character in the book even though you never see him? If your answer is yes, draw a picture in your notebook of the way you think he looks.
3. What mistake did Amin make each time he counted the camels? If you had been one of the children who shared Amin's secret, would you have kept it a secret? Why?
4. When did you first realize why Amin kept "losing one camel"?

5. Amin was worried because he had no blue beads to frighten away the Evil One. Can you think of other good-luck charms that people carry? A fear of some unknown bad luck is called a superstition. Do you know people who are superstitious about letting black cats cross their paths? What other superstitions do you know?
6. Do you think Amin will worry about the Evil One if he forgets the beads the next trip he makes? Why?
7. *Nine in a Line,* like any good story, has a beginning, a middle, and an end. Which part did you like best? Why? Draw a picture for each part that shows what that part was about.

TALKING IT OVER

You may want to share your ideas about these questions with others who have read *Nine in a Line.*

1. Amin showed that he was a good sport when he laughed at his own mistake. Do you remember any time when the joke was on you and you were able to laugh at yourself?
2. Have you read the story *The Emperor's New Clothes?* Can you think of a way in which this story is like *Nine in a Line?*
3. It has been said that the life of the Bedouin depends on the camel. Can you think of any reasons why the camel is so important to him?
4. If you were a sheik, would you hire Amin to do a job for you? Why?

WHAT MAKES A FOLK TALE?

Nine in a Line is a very old Arabic folk tale. Folk tales are stories that were told for hundreds of years before they were written down. Some folk tales have magic in them. Do you remember *Jack and the Beanstalk?*

Others, like *Beauty and the Beast* and *The Frog Prince*, are about animals who become human.

Nine in a Line is a folk tale about a simpleton, a rather silly person. But as in most folk tales of this kind, people help the simpleton, and he finally does what he set out to do. Think about the story once again before you answer these questions.

1. Who was the simpleton in *Nine in a Line*?
2. What job did the simpleton have to do in this story?
3. What problem does the simpleton have with his job?
4. What kind of people help the simpleton with his problem?
5. Does Amin finally do what he set out to do?

Tell of some other folk tales that you know. Are they about magic, animals that become human, simpletons, or something else?

PEOPLE OF THE DESERT

The story and pictures in *Nine in a Line* tell how people of the desert live. Number a page in your notebook from 1 – 7. Read the following sentences. If a sentence is true, put a *T* beside the right number. If a sentence is false, put an *F* beside the number and rewrite the sentence so that it is true. Use a piece of paper if you don't have a notebook.

1. Bedouins belong to tribes. Sheiks are leaders of the tribes.
2. Bedouins use camels for transportation in the desert.
3. The letters of the Arabic language look like ours.
4. No Arab woman covers her face when she is outside her home.
5. Bedouins wear flowing robes and a head covering. A twisted cord holds the covering in place.

6. Some Bedouin tribes live in tents.
7. People living in the desert get their water at an oasis.

LET'S PRETEND

Have you ever thought how many things you can act out without saying a word? You might want to do this with *Nine in a Line*. All of you have probably played you were a cowboy or an Indian galloping on a make-believe horse. Now you can ride a camel. Imagine how Amin first of all made a camel kneel, then slipped a bridle over his nose. Climb onto the kneeling camel's hump, as Amin did. Teeter back and forth as your camel gets to his feet.

Now as you ride along, rock backward and forward as Amin did. First let your camel walk. Then when you have become a better rider, let him jog-trot along. Of course you will also need to learn to ride backwards, so you can turn around and count the camels behind you.

Act as Amin did when he first counted the camels and discovered that one was "missing." You and others who have read the story can take turns playing the parts of Amin, the camels, the kind shepherd, the two women, and the children.

Before you play any part of the story, reread it and make pictures in your mind of what the characters did. How did each of them feel at certain times in the story? Get in mind the steps in which the action took place. Each time you play, it will be easier to remember what to do. Remember that you are acting out the story without speaking.

Perhaps Amin's trip back to the sheik's camp is the part of the story you like best. Climb back up on your camel and start riding again. Suddenly remember that the sheik forgot to buy blue beads for the camels. Worry as Amin did about the Evil One taking a camel. Try to feel as frightened and worried as he did before you turn around and count your line of camels. Feel as scared as Amin was as you count camel tracks and run searching here, there, and everywhere for the "missing" camel. Think how he felt when the kind shepherd found that he had nine camels! Take turns playing Amin and the shepherd. Imagine how the kind shepherd felt when he began to search for the lost camel. Imagine how he felt when he found that there were, indeed, nine camels.

You can have fun acting out the whole story or part of it. One of you can be the narrator or storyteller. This person reads or tells the story while the others in the group are acting it out.

You may remember other funny stories about silly people who did silly things. *The Six Foolish Fishermen* is one that is fun to read, to tell, and to act. Can you think of any others?

Amin had a good sense of humor. Do you think he would enjoy this poem?

THE CAMEL
by Ogden Nash

The camel has a single hump;
The dromedary two;
Or else the other way around.
I'm never sure. Are you?

ARITHMETIC
by Carl Sandburg

Arithmetic is where numbers fly like pigeons
    in and out of your head.

Arithmetic tells you how many you lose or
    win if you know how many you had
    before you lost or won.

Arithmetic is seven eleven all good children
    go to heaven — or five six bundle of sticks.

Arithmetic is numbers you squeeze from
    your head to your hand to your pencil
    to your paper till you get the answer.

From "Arithmetic" in COMPLETE POEMS, copyright, 1950, by Carl Sandburg. Reprinted by permission of Harcourt, Brace & World, Inc.

Arithmetic is where the answer is right and everything is nice and you can look out the window and see the blue sky — or the answer is wrong and you have to start all over and try again and see how it comes out this time.

The poet has given you some of his ideas about what arithmetic is. Amin might have said, "Arithmetic is counting nine camels in a line and remembering to count the one you're riding on." What are some of your ideas about what arithmetic is? Write them in your notebook.

COLLECTORS' ITEMS

RUN AWAY HABEEB!
by Gladys Yessayan Cretan

Habeeb's family had worked hard to send him to school. But the boys in his new school seemed unfriendly, so he ran away. Now his problem was to earn a living without being able to read or write.

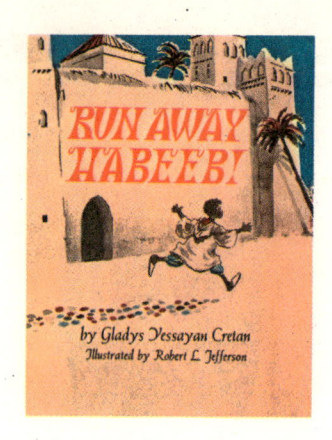

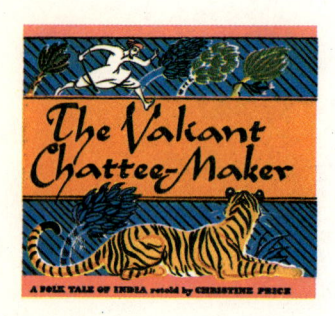

THE VALIANT CHATTEE-MAKER
retold by Christine Price

Can a man who mistakes a tiger for his donkey become famous? The Chattee-maker could . . . and did!

SIX FOOLISH FISHERMEN
by Benjamin Elkin

This story is taken from the same old tale as *Nine in a Line*. How are the stories alike? How are they different?

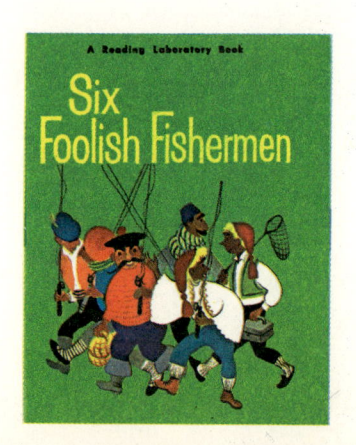

THE EMPEROR'S NEW CLOTHES
by Hans Christian Andersen

This is another colorful story in which children discover something that grown-ups pretend not to notice.

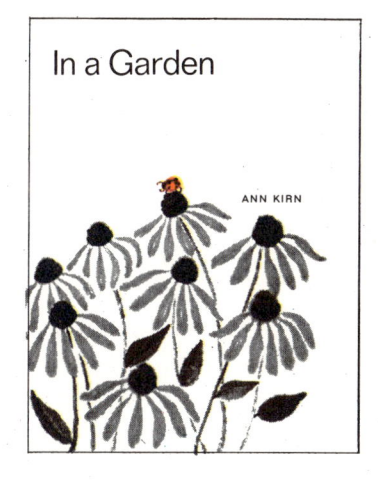

IN A GARDEN
by Ann Kirn

Everyone but Lady Bug had something to do in the garden circus. But when circus day came, the show couldn't have gone on without her.

MR. MOONLIGHT AND OMAR
by James Holding

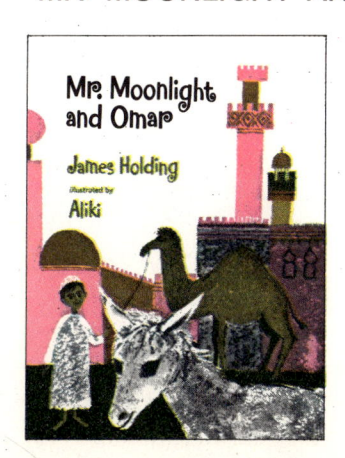

Omar is a bad-tempered camel. Mr. Moonlight is a kind and friendly donkey. Do you think these two would make good farm animals? You may be surprised.

SUMMER READING

AN ANTEATER NAMED ARTHUR
by Bernard Waber. Boston: Houghton Mifflin Company, 1967.

Arthur is often a problem to his mother. Sometimes he doesn't understand, sometimes he has nothing to do, and sometimes Arthur's room is more than his mother can believe.

THE BRAVE LITTLE GOAT OF MONSIEUR SÉGUIN
by Alphonse Daudet. Cleveland: The World Publishing Company, 1968.

Blanquette wasn't afraid of being eaten by the wolf. Like all the other goats, she just wanted to run off to the mountains and be free.

THE CRANE MAIDEN
by Miyoko Matsutani. New York: Parents' Magazine Press, 1968.

The lovely maiden agreed to weave her beautiful cloth for the old couple. But they must promise never to look in on her while she worked.

THE DAY THE SPACESHIP LANDED
by Beman Lord. New York: Henry Z. Walck, Inc., 1967.

Mike Davis really saw the spaceship land. He even talked with the men on board. But getting people to believe his story was something else.

MISSISSIPPI POSSUM
by Miska Miles. Boston: Little, Brown and Company, 1965.

When the Mississippi River overflows, the Jefferson family and a little gray possum share the same shelter.